LIFE SCIENCE LIBRARY

MAN AND SPACE

TIME
LIFE
BOOKS

LIFE SCIENCE LIBRARY

CONSULTING EDITORS
René Dubos
Henry Margenau
C. P. Snow

MAN AND SPACE

by Arthur C. Clarke
and the Editors of LIFE

TIME INCORPORATED, NEW YORK

ABOUT THIS BOOK

THIS BOOK reviews the history of man's interest in space and analyzes the technological developments that have enabled him to explore this new frontier. The book also discusses the future—not only describing travel to the moon and beyond but also reporting changes that may occur on earth as a consequence of experiments in space.

The volume consists of alternating text chapters and picture essays. Some of the essays complement material covered in the preceding chapter (for example, Chapter 5 and the accompanying essay both deal with unmanned satellites); others supplement the text chapters with new material (Chapter 8 discusses interstellar travel; Essay 8 describes the training of the astronauts who must make the journeys into space).

In the Appendix are a glossary of terms, a statistical chart of the planets, and a list of important events and people in space history.

THE AUTHOR

ARTHUR C. CLARKE has an international reputation as an authority on space and as a science-fiction writer; he has written some 30 books, published around the world in 200 editions. In 1945 he wrote a technical paper which first suggested the communications satellite; for this he was awarded a gold medal by the Franklin Institute. A Briton, Mr. Clarke was educated at Kings College, London, and is a past chairman of the British Interplanetary Society. He now lives in Ceylon.

THE CONSULTING EDITORS

RENE DUBOS, member and professor of The Rockefeller University, is a microbiologist and experimental pathologist world-famous for his pioneering in antibiotics, including the discovery of tyrothricin. He has written *Man Adapting* and is coauthor of *Health and Disease* in this series.

HENRY MARGENAU is Eugene Higgins professor of physics and natural philosophy at Yale, an editor of the *American Journal of Science* and a notable contributor to spectroscopy and nuclear physics. He has written *Open Vistas*, *The Nature of Physical Reality*, and is coauthor of *The Scientist* in this series.

C. P. SNOW, physicist and author, has won acclaim for his many novels, among them *The Affair* and *Corridors of Power*, which explore the relationship between the scientist and the rest of modern society. As Lord Snow, he was named to the British Ministry of Technology in 1964.

ON THE COVER

A huge Saturn I rocket roars off the pad at Cape Kennedy in one of the vital preliminaries to manned lunar exploration. Its second stage, which went into orbit weighing almost 19 tons, was designed as forerunner for the third stage of the Apollo moon vehicle.

CONTENTS

TIME-LIFE BOOKS

EDITOR
Norman P. Ross

EXECUTIVE EDITOR
Maitland A. Edey

TEXT DIRECTOR   **ART DIRECTOR**
Jerry Korn   Edward A. Hamilton

CHIEF OF RESEARCH
Beatrice T. Dobie

Assistant Text Director: Harold C. Field
Assistant Art Director: Arnold C. Holeywell
Assistant Chiefs of Research:
Monica O. Horne, Martha Turner

PUBLISHER
Rhett Austell

General Manager: Joseph C. Hazen Jr.
Planning Director: Frank M. White
Business Manager: John D. McSweeney
Circulation Director: Joan D. Manley
Publishing Board: Nicholas Benton, Louis Bronzo,
James Wendell Forbes, John S. Wiseman

LIFE MAGAZINE

EDITOR: Edward K. Thompson
MANAGING EDITOR: George P. Hunt
PUBLISHER: Jerome S. Hardy

LIFE SCIENCE LIBRARY

SERIES EDITOR: Martin Mann
Editorial staff for *Man and Space:*
Editor: Robert Claiborne
Associate Editor: Robert G. Mason
Text Editor: Alfred Lansing
Picture Editor: Simone Daro Gossner
Designer: Arnold C. Holeywell
Associate Designer: Edwin Taylor
Staff Writers: Tom Alexander, Simon Johnson,
Jonathan Kastner, Harvey B. Loomis,
Gerald Simons, Paul Trachtman
Chief Researcher: Thelma C. Stevens
Researchers: Leah Dunaief, Norbert S. Baer,
Elizabeth Evans, Ann Ferebee,
Donald Hinkle, Robert R. McLaughlin,
Donald Newton, Victor H. Waldrop
EDITORIAL PRODUCTION
Color Director: Robert L. Young
Copy Staff: Marian Gordon Goldman,
Suzanne Seixas, Dolores A. Littles
Picture Bureau: Margaret K. Goldsmith,
Joan Lynch
Art Assistants: Douglas B. Graham,
Patricia Byrne, Charles Mikolaycak

This book, from its conception to final editing, was under the professional direction of Arthur C. Clarke. The text chapters were written by Mr. Clarke, the picture essays by the editorial staff. The following individuals and departments of Time Inc. were helpful in the production of the book: Ralph Crane, Fritz Goro and Ralph Morse, LIFE staff photographers; John Dille, LIFE Senior Editor; Albert Rosenfeld, LIFE Associate Editor; Margaret Sargent, LIFE film editor; Doris O'Neil, Chief, LIFE Picture Library; Richard M. Clurman, Chief, TIME-LIFE News Service; and Peter Draz, Chief, Bureau of Editorial Reference.

INTRODUCTION

As THE WIFE of Robert H. Goddard, I have had the profound privilege of observing at firsthand the evolution toward realization of one of man's most breathtaking dreams. The pattern of this evolution was not unusual. First, the orderly beauty of mathematics was used to supply proof of a possibility. Then, in the laboratory and the field, the intuitions of the research scientist—the "searcher obedient to the command of truth" —bridged the gap between theory and reality, and laid down general lines upon which technicians and engineers could build. Third, an immense flowering of ingenuity succeeded in designing and improving thousands of components. It was in the first and second steps that my husband was able to make a contribution. He was not to live to see the third.

But although the pattern of development was recognizable, even in my husband's time it was clear that this scientific undertaking differed in an important respect from those that had gone before. It early became apparent that the aspiration implicit in high-altitude exploration had a tremendous appeal to the general public. Perhaps people sensed that space travel was the next rung on what Sir Richard Burton called the "ladder infinite-stepped" upon which mankind had emerged from the ocean to the shoreline, to the dry land, the mountains and the air. Now space exploration, a dream as old as history, lay within reach.

I have lived to see a great intellectual explosion in which the frontiers of all man's knowledge have been extended—and it is only a beginning. As the great lunar missiles go aloft, the best minds in many scientific disciplines will continue to be focused upon these instruments. Millions of other men all over the world, watching in fascination, will be vividly reminded that science itself is of immediate concern and importance to them. Surely no experiments were ever followed with such wonder by so many as the Sputnik and Mercury series of space shots. Here was high drama and romance combined with superb science. Now we are all beginning to try seriously to imagine the nature of the planets and galaxies, "all surely going somewhere," as Whitman has said.

Perhaps I shall not see Saturn V's successors. But I am sure, as my husband was, that they will achieve for the mind and spirit of mankind unparalleled heights of grandeur.

—Esther C. Goddard

1

The Dreamers and the Doers

"Earth is the cradle of the mind, but one cannot live in the cradle forever."

K. E. TSIOLKOVSKY

VERY LITTLE THAT IS WORTHWHILE is ever achieved without dreams. But to be fruitful, dreams must be controlled by reason and founded on reality. Though men have speculated about space travel for more than 2,000 years, it was not until the beginning of the 17th Century that those speculations had any scientific basis. In 1609 Galileo Galilei turned the newly invented telescope upon the heavens, and became the first of all men to see (however dimly through the chromatic haze of his crude lenses) that there were worlds beyond the earth. He saw the sharp-edged shadows of great mountains arranged across the lonely lunar plains. He glimpsed, but could not understand, the enigma of Saturn's rings. He saw Venus as a tiny, dazzling crescent, waxing and waning like a distant moon. Above all, he discovered four sparks of light orbiting the planet Jupiter, and so destroyed forever the belief that all the heavenly bodies revolved around the earth. Indeed, if Jupiter possessed four satellites while the earth had but one, perhaps man was not as important in the celestial scheme as he had fondly imagined.

Within a century, the closed and tidy medieval cosmos, which contained only Heaven, earth and Hell like a three-story building, had vanished into oblivion. We find perhaps its last traces in *Paradise Lost* (1667), and even there it is obvious that Milton is well aware of the new astronomy and the vast scale of the real universe. Only a single lifetime earlier, Shakespeare's "Doubt thou that the stars are fire, / Doubt that the Sun doth move" had continued to pay tribute to the idea of a fixed central earth and a revolving heaven. Between these two masters of the English language lies the Great Divide which we call the Copernican Revolution.

For it was the Polish astronomer Nicholas Copernicus who in the 15th Century paved the way for the modern picture of the universe by publishing a theory of the solar system in which the sun is the central body and the earth is merely one of the planets revolving around it. Two other scientists established this theory beyond dispute. First in the 17th Century Johannes Kepler, after years of patient calculation and endless detours down mathematical blind alleys, discovered the laws that govern the movements of the planets—and which today control the movements of those artificial planets, our space probes. The simplest and most surprising of Kepler's three laws was the first: planets do not—as everyone, including Copernicus, had supposed—travel around the sun in perfect circles. They follow that considerably more complex curve, the ellipse.

Then in the next generation came the great Newton, banishing the last

ATTIRED FOR SPACE
A technician tests a space suit in simulated moon conditions—a Mojave desert lava cave. By the time the first deep-space voyagers actually depart, tens of thousands of tests will have been made, so that every conceivable exigency can be met and overcome. For example, this suit allows its wearer to pull his arms inside for the vital luxury of scratching an itch.

traces of metaphysics from the heavens, and turning the solar system into one vast machine whose every movement is explained by a single all-embracing law—the Law of Universal Gravitation. The celestial matter of the heavenly bodies and the gross matter of this earth obey the same rules: no longer could any distinction be drawn between them.

And so a strange paradox occurred: as the new telescopes multiplied the scale of the universe beyond all the dreams of earlier ages, the new knowledge made this vastly expanded universe understandable and even familiar. Astronomy ceased to belong to the theologians and became a sort of extension of geography.

All these discoveries—occurring as they did at the same time as a great surge in terrestrial exploration—affected every field of human thought and culture. Not only did they give impetus to the development of modern science and technology; they also acted as a stimulus to imagination. A few decades after the first telescope, a whole literature of space travel had sprung up, merging fiction with the newly acquired astronomical knowledge *(pages 16 to 29)*.

Using fiction to sow facts

One of these works was by the great Kepler himself. There is something appropriate in the fact that the first attempt at scientific space fiction was by the man whose laws shape the paths of all vehicles that now travel beyond the earth.

In Kepler's *Somnium* (Sleep) the spirits which carry people to the moon can make the journey only at one special time: during the fleeting moment of eclipse, when a bridge of shadow spans the gulf between earth and its satellite—a beautiful concept which proves that Kepler, like all great scientists, was also a poet.

It is not surprising that Kepler found the moon inhabited—but it is worth noting that he made a serious attempt to invent occupants who were not merely displaced human beings, but creatures biologically adapted to a world of unearthly conditions. Despite its employment of spirits, *Somnium* was *authentic* science fiction. It thus established a tradition that flourished for three and a half centuries—but it also inaugurated another that is coming to an end. There will always be stories of flights to other worlds, but now that fact is catching up with fiction the moon will no longer be the goal.

After Kepler came a host of imitators, few of whose works now have much interest either as science or as fiction. Yet they served a useful purpose, for they spread knowledge of the new astronomical ideas, and sometimes conveyed accurate information to their readers. They filled a role not unlike that of the comic strips that, in our own generation, prepared millions of youngsters for the age of space. Sometimes it is

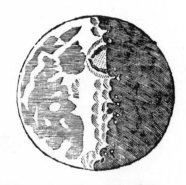

DISCOVERING THE REAL MOON

Galileo focused his telescope on the skies one night in 1609 and discovered "the most beautiful and delightful sight"—that the moon was not the smooth disk it was then thought to be. It was a world crossed by mountains and valleys. He published his findings in a booklet, "Sidereus Nuncius" (Starry Messenger). In it was the woodcut shown above, crude compared to today's photographs of the moon, but extremely accurate.

more important to fire the imagination than to be the slave of fact.

The most ingenious of the 17th Century literary astronauts was the flamboyant Cyrano de Bergerac. Cyrano operated on the grand scale: not only did he travel to the moon—he also went to the sun. And he devised several means of propulsion, including rockets and a sun-powered jet device. Despite their appearance of accuracy, these anticipations cannot be regarded as anything more than pure flukes; Cyrano de Bergerac certainly did not realize that in mentioning the rocket he had hit upon the only method of propulsion that could operate in the vacuum of space.

The vacuum of space. It was some time before the fiction writers appreciated the implications of this unpleasant fact of astronomical life. In the early days, no one (except Kepler, as might have been expected) had drawn much distinction between flight inside the atmosphere and flight beyond it. Indeed, there were some who felt that the earth's atmosphere might extend all the way to the moon. It would take a little longer to get to the moon than, for example, to the new American colonies, but the technology required for both feats would be the same.

This naive attitude was no longer possible after 1783, when the first passenger balloon left the ground. As men began to explore the hitherto inaccessible sky, they soon discovered that there was a limit to their vertical travels. At a mere hundred-thousandth of the distance to the moon, the air became cold and difficult to breathe. A little higher—only a miserable five or six miles from the ground—unconsciousness and death were waiting. The road to the stars, which the balloon had appeared to open, was more firmly closed than ever.

Who might be there?

And so, for more than half a century, the dream of space travel languished. But there was no lack of interest in astronomy, or in the idea of life on other worlds. Philosophers, writers, scientists speculated about planets, imagining the types of beings who might inhabit them and even suggesting means of communication. Signs of intelligent life were sought on the scarred face of the moon, and upon the more distant planets. Needless to say, some astronomers believed that they had found such signs, but no one took them seriously. Still less did anyone take seriously the idea that it might really be possible, one day, not merely to communicate with the planets, but to reach them.

Jules Verne did as much as any man to change this attitude. His *From the Earth to the Moon*, published in 1865, was virtually an engineering blueprint of a space project, facing up to all the technical difficulties and making a brave try at solving them. Verne, with his excellent knowledge of science and engineering, understood very clearly that the basic problem of space flight was to achieve sufficient initial

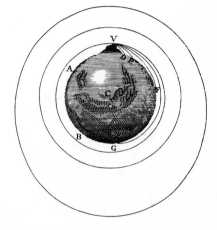

NEWTON'S FALLING ORBIT
Starting with the fact that a thrown object falls in a curve as a result of the pull of gravity, Sir Isaac Newton developed the theory of orbital flight. In his drawing shown above, he illustrated that an object hurled from an imaginary mountain, *V,* would fall to *D.* If the object were thrown harder, it would fall to *E;* harder still, to *F* or *G.* Finally, if it were thrown from some point in space, it would "fall" around the world *(outer circles).*

speed to escape from the earth. Although the giant gun he proposed was a poor solution, by one of the odder coincidences of literature he placed this launching device 150 miles from Cape Kennedy. Across a century of time and the width of the Atlantic, that is not bad shooting.

Verne himself was probably well aware of his "space gun's" defects. The gun aside, his over-all approach was entirely scientific. The whole story radiates a confidence that technology could solve any problem presented to it. *From the Earth to the Moon* is still worth reading for its humor, insight and occasional startling anticipations. Almost certainly Verne was the first to suggest today's experimental space medicine; the members of his Gun Club tested their theories by firing a cat and a squirrel in a hollow mortar shell. The cat survived the acceleration; the squirrel did not survive the cat.

There is also a distinctly modern touch in Verne's account of the fierce competition between Florida and Texas for the honor of providing the launching site; 90 years later, Congress and United States space officials were involved in just this rivalry. But even Verne could never have dreamed that one day the entire budget he proposed for the moonshot would be poured into space by the United States before lunchtime every day of the week.

Verne, like Kepler, had many now-forgotten imitators; from his day to this, the flood of space literature has never ceased. Out of it all, only the works of the young H. G. Wells are of any permanent value. *The First Men in the Moon* and *The War of the Worlds* are timeless museum pieces, which will still be read for enjoyment generations hence.

A "brick moon" in orbit

One other tale, however, is worth rescuing briefly from oblivion. In 1870 the *Atlantic Monthly* published a serial by the Boston clergyman Edward Everett Hale which contains the very first suggestion ever made for an artificial satellite. Hale's *The Brick Moon* is in some ways a remarkably farsighted piece of work. The author pointed out that an easily visible body revolving around the earth in a close orbit would be invaluable to navigators at sea; today's Transit satellites are a realization of Hale's concept (although the Transits utilize radio techniques). To be visible to the naked eye, Hale's Brick Moon had to be 200 feet in diameter—close enough to the 100 feet of the spectacular Echo I. Though Hale's method of launching, a spinning flywheel, was as impractical as Verne's, his choice of brick as a structural material was well thought out. He considered that it was the best stuff to withstand the heat of atmospheric friction; he thus anticipated today's interest in ceramics for nose cones and re-entry vehicles.

By the time the 20th Century dawned, man was about to conquer the

A LAMPOON ASTRONAUT

Nineteenth Century satirists found much to laugh about in schemes to rocket into space. The buckaroo riding his steam bronc in an 1849 cartoon at left says: "I wish Jemima could see me now, goin through the Firmament like a streak of greased lightnin on a Telegraph wire; I guess she'd feel a sorter vexed that she didn't pack up her fixins and go long."

air—but in the small town of Kaluga, 100 miles south of Moscow, a deaf schoolteacher named Konstantin Eduardovich Tsiolkovsky was dreaming of the stars.

Tsiolkovsky, born in 1857, had become passionately interested in science at an early age, and though he was largely self-taught, he had a sound grasp of physics and mathematics. After an early flirtation with aeronautics, he became obsessed with the problem of space travel. He was one of the first men to realize that the rocket provided a means of escaping from the earth. As early as 1898, he had derived the fundamental mathematical laws of rocket motion upon which the design of all space vehicles is based. In 1903—the year of Kitty Hawk—he published his main results and laid the foundations of astronautics.

But he did much more. He foresaw space exploration as part of a continuing social process which would eventually transform human life and spread it throughout the solar system. To advance his ideas, he poured out a stream of articles, both popular and scientific, and wrote a remarkable novel, *Outside the Earth*, which was a fictionalized account of his theories.

How to take a bath in space

Even today, the breadth of Tsiolkovsky's vision is most impressive. When the first airplanes were staggering off the ground, he was writing about satellites, solar energy, "ether suits" (we now call them spacesuits), the use of plants to provide food and fresh oxygen on long journeys, and the colonization of the solar system. He even considered such minor, but far from unimportant, matters as the problem of baths in weightless spaceships. (His solution: centrifugal showers.)

It is the usual fate of prophets to be ridiculed and ignored by their contemporaries, but Tsiolkovsky was fortunate. By the latter part of his long life, his genius was fully appreciated, and his works were reprinted widely throughout the U.S.S.R. By the 1930s he was something of a national hero. A monumental encyclopedia on interplanetary communication was published in Leningrad between 1928 and 1932 (a remarkably early date); one entire volume of it was devoted to Tsiolkovsky. When he died in 1935 he received a state funeral.

Most of the outside world paid little attention to this long and sustained Russian interest in space travel. But the rising tide of technology and science, and the rapid conquest of the air, made it inevitable that others would follow in Tsiolkovsky's footsteps, deriving the same results quite independently. Before the first World War, a young New England physics professor named Robert Hutchings Goddard *(pages 62-73)* became interested in rockets as a means of overcoming the altitude limitations of balloons. His 1919 pamphlet, "A Method of Reaching Extreme Alti-

WELLS'S WAR OF THE WORLDS
Three-legged Mars men attack earth and incinerate Chobham, England, in H. G. Wells's *The War of the Worlds*. All attempts to stop these tripodians failed, and they were about to take over the earth when they were finally subdued by earth bacteria. Scientists today feel that Mars's bacteria might win the "war" if returning Mars-ships are not decontaminated.

tudes," was an entirely mathematical analysis of what we today call the meteorological sounding rocket, capable of carrying instruments to heights no airborne vehicles can attain. It would never have attracted much attention outside scientific circles—if Goddard had not added a brief postscript pointing out that the same principle of rocket propulsion could also be used to land a visible charge of flash-powder on the moon.

Perhaps this was a tactical mistake; by associating himself with something as obviously crazy as moon rockets, Goddard laid himself open to ridicule and sensational journalism. Nevertheless, a few farsighted individuals appreciated the value of his work; with their help he was able to continue experimenting through the '20s and '30s. In 1926, at Auburn, Massachusetts, he launched the first liquid-propelled rocket. It flew a distance of 184 feet, thus beating the Wrights' initial performance by a few yards. In the long perspective of history, it may emerge as the more important flight; the airplane merely gave swifter passage to lands already known; the rocket opened the gate to the stars.

Goddard—as his notebooks disclose—was fully aware of his work's implications, but a natural caution kept him from making public pronouncements about space flight. The third pioneer of astronautics had no such qualms, and perhaps because of this fact his ideas had a much greater immediate impact upon the world.

A city architect's plan

It is curious that the Romanian Hermann Oberth, like Tsiolkovsky and Goddard, earned his living as a teacher; presumably the academic life gave all three men both the leisure and the training for their speculations. In 1923 Oberth published, largely at his own expense, a slim booklet whose title may be translated as *The Rocket into Interplanetary Space*. He arrived at the same conclusions as his Russian and American precursors, but he also went a good deal beyond them. He not only outlined theoretical designs of high-altitude research rockets and man-carrying spaceships, but he also revived the idea of the large manned satellite or space station, which had been more or less forgotten since Hale's *Brick Moon*, half a century before.

Oberth's speculations attracted surprising interest, especially in Germany, where they started a chain reaction. Other technical books on the subject appeared, the most notable being a purely mathematical study of interplanetary rocket trajectories by—of all people—the city architect of Essen. Twenty years later this man, Dr. Walter Hohmann, was killed in the air raids that destroyed his city, but the brochure he published in 1925 has given him a certain immortality. The men who now launch space probes to the moon and planets talk about "Hohmann orbits" every day, as the most economical routes across the solar system.

The most important result of Oberth's book was not that it led to more theorizing but that it inspired actual experimentation. Little rocket societies sprang up in many countries: the Verein für Raumschiffahrt (Society for Space Travel) in Germany in 1927 (Oberth later became its president), the Gruppa Isutcheniya Reaktivnovo Dvisheniya (Group for Investigation of Reaction Motion) in Russia in 1928, the American Interplanetary (later Rocket) Society in 1930, the British Interplanetary Society in 1933. Students and young engineers, with few resources but much enthusiasm, started to design and build rockets.

Of course, men had been making rockets for centuries. During all that time, the basic principles had remained unchanged. Gunpowder was packed into a hollow tube, and on ignition the hot gases escaped from a nozzle, producing a violent, brief and uncontrollable burst of acceleration. This was good enough for fireworks and short-range weapons; it was useless for space flight, where sustained power would be needed over long periods of time. Moreover, the classical gunpowder rocket is extremely inefficient.

In his early experiments, Goddard had made major improvements in the performance of powder rockets by using special nozzles, but he soon decided (as Tsiolkovsky had done a generation earlier) that there was a better answer. This involved switching from gunpowder-type solid fuels to combustible liquids like gasoline and liquid oxygen. Pound for pound, such mixtures contain several times as much energy as high explosives; a can of ordinary gasoline will release far more energy than the same weight of dynamite or TNT. Moreover, rockets which burn liquid fuels can be controlled; the thrust can be shut off at the turn of a valve, or throttled back by reducing the rate of flow. On all counts (except simplicity) the liquid rocket should be superior to one using solid fuels.

The trouble with liquids

Experts now know that the situation is not quite so clear-cut as this, but in 1930 liquid-propelled rockets appeared to be the only answer to the problem of space flight. Yet apart from Goddard (whose work was still largely unpublished and unknown), nobody had ever built a rocket *motor*. Many experts believed that if you squirted liquid oxygen and gasoline together you would get only a violent explosion.

It was just as well that the young enthusiasts of the '30s did not know that it would take tens of years and billions of dollars to solve the gigantic problems they were tackling with such puny resources. Only in two countries—Germany and Russia—did the pioneer rocket men receive the support essential for serious progress. And their backers, it is hardly necessary to say, were interested mainly in military objectives.

Rocketeer-writer Willy Ley, now in America, has recorded the tragi-

EARLY ROCKETRY

Even in prehistoric times, a form of rocket was developed in Asia for use as fireworks. These early rockets were made by packing saltpeter and charcoal into bamboo tubes. Combinations of tubes, some six inches in diameter, were bound with split cane, then launched from bamboo mortars. The art reached its highest development in Japan, as shown in this print.

comic history of the Verein für Raumschiffahrt. Ley, vice president of the organization, and Oberth, its president, were hired to build a rocket to promote a movie, *The Girl in the Moon* (director Fritz Lang; script, Frau Lang). The rocket was never completed, but the movie was, and in the course of its production Fritz Lang invented the countdown which has since held whole nations glued to their TV sets.

As for the Verein für Raumschiffahrt, it proved to the world that the theories of the rocketeers were correct. It also attracted the interest of the German Army, notably in the shape of one Captain Walter Dornberger, doctor of engineering. Captain Dornberger, a shrewd judge of men and machines, was not impressed by the VfR, but he was impressed by a teen-age student who was helping the society in his spare time. So the Army hired the student, whose name was Wernher von Braun.

In utter secrecy, the German rocket effort grew—first at Kummersdorf, near Berlin, and after 1937 at Peenemünde, on the shores of the Baltic. Soon thousands of engineers and scientists, not too upset by the fact that Hitler did not believe in rockets, were working to produce the giant missile the world was later to know as the V-2.

Amid screaming wind tunnels and flaming test stands, the centuries of ineffectual visions and idle reveries were drawing to a close. At Peenemünde, the power would meet the dream.

Pursuit of an Ancient Vision

When man began to unravel the mysteries of the universe at first hand, he was merely acting out one of his oldest and most cherished pastimes: armchair space travel. He has been playing at this game, in mythology and in literature, since ancient times—in the tales of the ancient Greeks, in the novels of Jules Verne, in the stories of contemporary science-fiction writers. Most of this storytelling has been more wild-eyed than thoughtful: launching devices for fictional space trips have included everything from the waxed bird feathers shown in the imaginative illustration opposite to giant cannon which fired a three-man projectile to the moon. But some of the thinking about space travel in past centuries has been remarkably farsighted, anticipating many of the problems modern man has faced as he has ventured into space. Whether impractical or scientific, all thinkers about space travel have agreed on one point: the trip is worth making.

AN EARLY CASUALTY IN SPACE
Icarus was the astronaut of Greek mythology. According to the legend, he and his father Daedalus ventured into the heavens on wings of wax and feathers. Though Daedalus warned his son not to fly too near the sun, the youth ignored the warning. He went too close, melted his wings, fell into the sea and drowned—the earliest, although legendary, casualty of space exploration.

A whirlwind whisks up the bark
containing Lucian and his shipmates
in a scene from his book "True History."
After an airborne voyage of seven days,
the voyagers arrive at a large,
circular, illuminated island: the moon.

Among the strange soldiers Lucian
meets on the moon are the
Windrunners, who sail into battle
propelled by wind in their great
shirts. Above the Windrunner, a
Spider Engineer spins a cobweb trap
from the moon to the morning star.

A Wild, Windborne Lunar Visit

The first known science-fiction writer was a Syrian named Lucian, who lived in the Second Century A.D. A lawyer who turned to itinerant lecturing, Lucian became a great success in the far corners of the Roman Empire. Then, abundantly endowed with experience, wealth and cynicism, he retired to Athens to try his hand as a writer and satirist. His book *True History* purports to be the story of a ship's company of 50 men whose vessel encounters a fierce storm in the Atlantic and is blown to the moon. Caught in a war between the moon people and the inhabitants of the sun, the ship's crew encounters a strange assortment of combatants *(left)*.

Despite the book's title, Lucian did not intend it to be taken seriously. It was a spoof, written in archaic Greek, poking fun at such solemn literary figures as Homer, Thucydides and Herodotus. Just in case his readers missed the point, Lucian warned in an introduction that the book was fictional. "So all readers beware," he concluded. "Don't believe any of it."

Cavalry of the Moon King rides into battle on three-headed buzzards (top), accompanied by saladbirds feathered with lettuce leaves. Also in the tale are such odd creatures as peashooters and garlickeers, as well as bowmen who ride fleas 12 times the size of elephants. In the book, the war between moon and sun ends in a truce, and Lucian sails back to earth for more adventures.

A contemplative Leonardo studies
the elements of flight and some designs
derived from his investigations.

Birds, Leonardo believed, held
the secret of flight—a secret,
he said "within the capacity of man
to reproduce." But first,
he said, it was necessary to
probe "the science of the winds."

A Great Student of Birds and Flight

One creative man who had a completely scientific interest in flight was the painter Leonardo da Vinci. Between 1486 and 1514, he designed several flight devices, including a glider, helicopter and parachute. Leonardo is believed to have tested models of these, and there is even a story, never substantiated, that he attempted flight in one machine.

Da Vinci's experiments fell roughly into two groups: the study of flight in birds, and the formation of laws of aerodynamics. In both enterprises he worked along scientific lines. For example, his design for a parachute (which he called a "tent roof") was based on the sound theory that "an object offers as much resistance to the air as the air does to the object." Someday, Leonardo believed, man would emulate the birds. "A bird," he wrote, "is an instrument working according to mathematical law. . . . Such an instrument constructed by man is lacking in nothing except the life of the bird, and this life must needs be supplied from that of man."

Leonardo's helicopter (top), driven by a spring, bites into the air as a screw bites into wood. He suggested making the helical vane of linen stiffened with starch.

The first design for an aircraft wing, as shaped on Leonardo's drawing board, resembled that of a bat. His cryptic mirror writing, above the wing, may have been intended as a code.

En route to the moon, space travelers of Johannes Kepler's science-fiction tale "Somnium" are propelled by spirits. Too careful a scientist to guess at a mode of transportation, Kepler cast his story in the form of a dream, and thus avoided the problem.

Kepler: More Science than Fiction

Johannes Kepler was a 17th Century astronomer, the first of a long and distinguished line of truly scientific science-fiction writers. Kepler was the first man to explain the natural laws of planetary motion; it was a desire to disseminate this information that led him to write fiction.

Kepler's allegorical work *Somnium, or the Astronomy of the Moon*, is similar in form to Lucian's *True History*. But where Lucian offered fantasy, Kepler offered fact, much of it centuries ahead of its time. Of the rigors of space flight Kepler reports the "initial movement is most uncomfortable and dangerous, for the traveler is torn aloft . . . as if blown up by gunpowder." In the stratosphere the astronaut encounters "bitter cold and lack of air to breathe." He experiences weightlessness and is slowed down by something comparable to reverse thrust as he approaches the moon, lest he "suffer injuries from too heavy a landing." Finally, *Somnium* contains a brilliant guess about the moon's topography and its climate.

Kepler peopled the moon with tough-hided creatures who spent most of the day in caves to escape the broiling sun.
His purpose in creating these characters was to emphasize the extremes of the moon's climate. He also
provided an amazingly accurate description of its surface.

23

Rising with the dew, Cyrano heads toward
the moon, propelled by vials of moisture.
Later, trying to return to France,
he landed instead in North America—because
(according to the book) the earth spun
under him while he was airborne. Actually,
of course, this escapade is based
on a fallacy, because an object in
the atmosphere moves with the turning earth.

Sailing into space, Cyrano
utilizes solar energy on a
lunar voyage. Sharply
focused sunlight, he explained,
drove the air out of the box
in some fashion. The resulting
vacuum caused more air to
rush in from below, propelling
the vehicle upward. The
sail was intended for steering.

The Weird Schemes of a Poet Cavalier

A few years after Kepler offered up science in the guise of fiction, a famous Frenchman wrote a work which presented a stew of wit, nonsense and parody under the cloak of science.

No writer ever thought up more novel ways to travel in space than the roistering poet Cyrano de Bergerac in his book *Voyages to the Moon and Sun*. Cyrano's hero first reasons that the sun causes the morning dew to rise, so he goes aloft by attaching vials filled with dew to his body. Next he tries a vehicle that anticipates the airplane (it has wings and a propeller), but on his takeoff from a rock tumbles ignominiously into the valley below. He greases his body with beef marrow to soothe his wounds—and finally gets to the moon because (and here Cyrano cites a superstition of the era) "I knew that at the time the moon was waning and that during this quarter she is wont to suck up the marrow of animals." Later he returns to earth and builds still another space vehicle *(center)*, in some respects the most wonderful of all.

Magnetic propulsion is demonstrated by the prophet Elijah, whom Cyrano met on the moon. Elijah tossed a magnetized ball skyward—and it pulled his metal ship along behind.

Space travel by goose-power, described by British author Francis Godwin in 1638, reappears in Cyrano's work when he encounters Godwin's hero on the moon.

25

In the first equestrian ascent, one of various 18th Century stunts, Pierre Testu-Brissy rises over Paris in 1798. He was also the first to fly at night.

An early French balloonist, Jean Pierre Blanchard (top) waves a flag over Brussels in 1786. His rig included two balloons and a parachute. Blanchard earlier had shared the first Channel crossing with John Jeffries, an American doctor. Later, in 1793, he introduced balloon-flying to America at Philadelphia. The paddle-equipped aeronaut at bottom is from a book published about 1802.

Under the Union Jack, the Italian diplomat Vincenzo Lunardi ascends over London in a gaudy gondola in 1785. A year earlier he made the first manned flight in England.

By Gas Bag to the Edges of Space

On November 21, 1783, the dream as old as history became a fact. On that day two Frenchmen, Jean Pilâtre de Rozier and the Marquis d'Arlandes, flew over Paris in a balloon, traveling five and a half miles in 25 minutes. Within a decade other balloon flights had been made in England, Germany, the United States, Belgium and the Netherlands. Space flight appeared imminent—for its risks and rigors were not understood—and several would-be astronauts died from lack of oxygen in high-flying attempts before the truth was learned.

In the interim, however, balloons enjoyed a spectacular popularity. Stunt flying became a favorite spectator sport, basic balloon design underwent marvelous modifications and skeptics were overwhelmed. Two aeronauts made a Channel crossing in 1785—with hardly an inch to spare —and Pilâtre was attempting a more ambitious one when the hydrogen in his 37-foot balloon caught fire. Thus the first man to fly was also the first one to be killed in a flying accident.

Hot air from a straw fire lifts the most famous balloon of all, the one used in the first manned flight.
The balloon was made of paper and linen by two French paper manufacturers, the brothers Joseph and Etienne Montgolfier. The ornate bag, 33 feet in diameter, rose 1,000 feet, carrying a pair of daring passengers.

Jules Verne and His Cannon Express

The most famous of all science-fiction writers was the 19th Century novelist Jules Verne, who conducted his heroes on journeys 20,000 leagues under the sea, around the world in 80 days and, inevitably, *From the Earth to the Moon* and *Around the Moon*.

Like all of his books, Verne's account of the lunar voyage was a careful amalgam of scientific accuracy, sound speculation and sheer imagination. His launching device, an enormous cannon, is a patent absurdity: its charge of 400,000 pounds of guncotton would have flattened the passengers without sending their lunar vehicle much higher than the nearby trees. But he correctly foresaw that a space capsule would have to attain a speed of 25,000 miles per hour to escape the earth's gravity, would become white-hot in the atmosphere and could be steered in flight by rockets. His account seemed so realistic that many readers refused to believe his lunar vehicle was fictional; some people, he reported in surprise, "really want to ride in my projectile."

A 900-foot cannon fires Verne's moon capsule into space (above). Stunned by the blast-off and terrified by a near collision with a meteoroid, the astronauts flounder in weightless wonder in their upholstered cabin (center). There was a report on earth that they had landed (right); actually, the book has them returning to earth without setting foot on the lunar surface.

2

The V-2
and the
Missile Art

"Do you realize what we accomplished today? Today the space ship was born!"

— GENERAL WALTER DORNBERGER
TO DR. WERNHER VON BRAUN,
October 3, 1942

WHEN A THING HAS BEEN DONE, it always looks easy. The years of effort, the mistakes and failures, the arguments with the experts who cried "Impossible!" are all forgotten. Instead, everyone asks: "Well, why did it take so long?"

Until 1942 no large rocket had ever left the ground. Only a handful of small liquid-propelled rockets had flown at all, most of them not very far and not very well. The V-2 (or A-4, the original German code name) was perhaps the greatest leap forward in technology that had ever been made up to that time. There was nothing comparable to it until, a few years later, the scientists of the Manhattan Project started designing multimillion-dollar, square-mile plants to produce a metal which had never before been made in quantities visible to the naked eye.

Because the basic components of the V-2 are at the heart of all space vehicles today—and will be for a long time to come—it is important to understand the problems that were faced in the German rocket program, and the manner in which they were solved.

It must be said at once that nobody "invented" the V-2. Almost all the parts that go into a large liquid-fuel rocket had been described by Konstantin Tsiolkovsky, Hermann Oberth and other pioneers. And the patient Dr. Goddard had done more: he had actually built and tested most of the basic rocket hardware. By 1935 he had successfully flown rockets weighing almost 100 pounds to heights of 7,500 feet.

The heart of a rocket, as of all vehicles, is its motor, or engine. A rocket engine is essentially an open-ended furnace in which fuel is burned at an unprecedented rate, the combustion products escaping at the highest possible velocity through a tapering nozzle. On paper, nothing looks simpler than a rocket engine, but it must safely confine such a concentration of heat, vibration and pressure that its design and testing may consume thousands of man-years and millions of dollars.

To toss a 14-ton missile 50 miles into the sky, the V-2 engine had to develop more than half a million horsepower—three times the power produced by the turbines of a giant liner like the *Queen Mary*. Yet the engine was scarcely over five feet long, and weighed about 1,000 pounds, achieving its enormous energy output by burning a mixture of alcohol and liquid oxygen at the then unheard-of rate of one ton every seven seconds. Though the temperature developed in the combustion chamber

CONTAINER FOR SPACE FUEL
Working inside the giant tank of a Mercury-Atlas booster, two missile technicians install anti-slosh baffles, which minimize shifting of the propellant inside the rocket. This tank contained 28,000 gallons; during the blast-off it emptied at the rate of 11,000 gallons per minute. The tanks of Saturn V will have a capacity almost 20 times greater than that of the Atlas.

was high enough to melt almost all metals in a few seconds, the V-2 engine was made of ordinary steel; the designers had intended to keep it from melting by using the alcohol fuel itself as a coolant. This system had worked on smaller rockets, but it proved insufficient here; the motors kept burning out at the nozzle. The trouble was finally overcome by injecting fuel around the nozzle so that it formed a protective film of vapor and shielded the vulnerable metal from the white-hot blast.

A fire pump to the rescue

To force one ton of propellant into the combustion chamber every seven seconds, against the back-pressure of the furiously burning gases, appeared to require something quite exceptional in the way of pumps. Wernher von Braun has recorded his surprise at discovering that a design based on ordinary fire-fighting pumps could do the job. But tremendous power was still needed—over 500 hp. Ordinarily, such power would require a motor weighing at least a ton—which would have left the rocket with no payload at all. The designers overcame this fundamental difficulty by developing a turbine only 24 inches in diameter, driven by superheated steam obtained from a chemical which had been manufactured for commercial and military purposes. This was concentrated hydrogen peroxide, an unstable substance which at the slightest provocation flashes into steam at a temperature of over 1,000° Fahrenheit. (The bottle labeled "hydrogen peroxide" in your medicine chest is perfectly safe; the chemical sold in the drugstore is about 95 per cent water.)

The propellants of the V-2 posed lesser problems. A rocket engine will operate, after a fashion, on almost anything that will burn; it is not a temperamental prima donna like the piston engine, which demands carefully refined petroleums further doctored with a host of additives. All a rocket needs is something that will burn smoothly, releasing the greatest possible amount of heat energy per pound of weight.

For this purpose, it is hard to improve upon such everyday chemicals as ethyl alcohol, kerosene or gasoline. Alcohol was used in the V-2; to it was added one-fourth part water to improve its performance. The alcohol was obtained from a very down-to-earth source: fermented potatoes.

A fuel, however, cannot supply energy by itself; it has to be combined with another substance—an oxidizer—to make combustion possible. By far the commonest oxidizer is the element from which the name is derived—oxygen. Ordinary engines—whether piston, turbine or old-fashioned steam—obtain their oxidizer from the surrounding air, which is one-fifth oxygen. The V-2, naturally, could not do this, since part of its powered flight would be beyond the atmosphere. It had to be entirely self-contained, carrying not only its own fuel but the oxidizer to burn it. This involved a considerable, but unavoidable, weight penalty; to burn

A SIMPLE ROCKET—THE BALLOON

This balloon shooting forward and a missile hurtling into space are propelled by similar forces. Air in a closed balloon exerts a uniform outward pressure. But air rushing out the neck (or the exhaust gases leaving rockets) unbalances this equilibrium, and results in an equal force on the surface opposite the neck, driving the balloon forward.

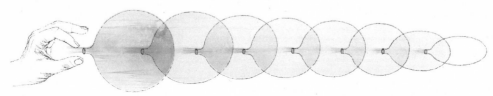

its four and a half tons of alcohol, the V-2 had to carry nearly five and a half tons of oxygen. This oxygen, of course, was not in the gaseous state; a storage tank with a capacity of 105,000 cubic feet would have been required. The V-2 used liquid oxygen—"lox"—which could be contained in a 154-cubic-foot tank.

Oxygen becomes a liquid only at low temperatures—at almost 300° below zero Fahrenheit. Handling tons of such a supercold substance demanded special techniques and storage facilities, but the rocket engineers were able to call upon the experience of industrial chemists, who had been using liquid oxygen for years.

A rocket, if it is to do anything more than provide a fireworks display, must be accurately guided. There is no great difficulty in making it alter its course, even when it is in the vacuum of space where normal aircraft-type rudders or fins would be useless. The rocket jet itself can provide steering as well as propulsion. The obvious way of doing this, as the V-2 designers were aware, is to mount the engine on gimbals, so that it can tilt back and forth, left and right. The changing direction of the jet will then alter the course of the vehicle, just as a swiveling outboard motor steers a powerboat. The day would come when most large rockets would be steered in this manner, but gimbals involved mechanical complexities which the V-2 designers preferred to avoid. They chose a simpler solution—small vanes, or rudders, inserted in the rocket jet itself.

It was then necessary to design some sort of robot brain to control these rudders, so that the missile could be steered to the desired target. Although radio control was an obvious possibility, it had grave military disadvantages because it might be jammed. Instead the V-2 used a revolutionary new guidance system, one which did not rely on any measurements, observations or signals from outside the rocket. Once it had been preset to steer the rocket across the 200 miles of space that was its maximum range, it could not be influenced or deflected by any external force. It was like the time lock of a bank vault, aimed irrevocably at some unchangeable moment in the future, beyond the further control even of its makers.

Guidance by hourglass

There is nothing mysterious about inertial guidance, the name given to this system; the basic idea is so simple it may seem surprising that it did not come into use many years before it did. But before it became practical it had to await the development of extremely sensitive yet rugged instruments, plus lightweight electronic computing systems.

Inertial guidance can best be demonstrated by that primitive symbol of Father Time—the hourglass. Imagine such a glass, standing inside a rocket at rest on the launching pad. Sand will flow through the neck,

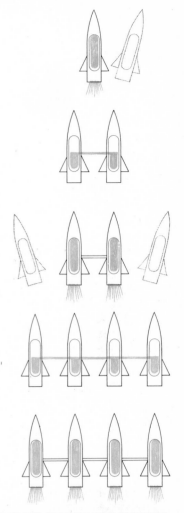

AN EARLY SCHEME FOR STAGING
The principle of staging rockets is similar to that of a plane jettisoning its empty wing tanks. This diagram shows a technique proposed by space pioneer Konstantin Tsiolkovsky in the 1920s. When half the fuel (blue) is burned, the rest is pumped into center tanks and the empty rockets dropped. The process is repeated until the last rocket reaches its goal.

ATTITUDE
GYROSCOPES

ACCELERATION
PERCEPTORS

ELECTRONIC
CONTROLS

FUEL CUTOFF
COMPUTER

ROCKET
MOTOR

STEERING
MOTORS

ROCKET
EXHAUST GASES

ROCKET EXHAUST
CONTROL VANE

ATMOSPHERIC
CONTROL VANE

INDEPENDENT ROCKET CONTROL

Inertial guidance allows rocketeers to send a missile on a predetermined path without signals from the ground. The guidance consists of two systems: flight controls *(gray)* that determine attitude; and acceleration controls *(blue)* that affect power. Gyroscopes are used in the attitude system to sense course deviations and relay flight changes or corrections through the electronic controls to the steering vanes in both systems. The acceleration control system cuts off fuel to the motor when the acceleration perceptors sense that a predetermined speed is reached. Thereafter, the rocket coasts to its target.

or constriction, and as long as the rocket does not move, the sand will accumulate in the lower container at a known, steady rate. If there is an ordinary clock beside the hourglass, the time shown by the two instruments will always agree.

Now suppose that the rocket blasts off, climbing vertically. Under the higher acceleration, the sand will flow through the hourglass more rapidly. In other words, it will run fast, and so gain on the clock. The rate at which it gains will depend on the rocket's acceleration—hence the rate will give an indication of the speed the vehicle has attained. It is clear that by comparing the clock and the hourglass, and making a few calculations, it would be possible to work out not only how fast the rocket was going, but also how high it had climbed. All this could be done automatically.

The V-2 used various devices that sensed the rocket's acceleration in this fashion. When the missile was on course and had attained the velocity needed to carry it to the target, the robot brain passed an order to the engine, cutting off the fuel. Thereafter, the missile coasted freely through space, as unguided as any artillery projectile. Usually the period under power lasted about one minute, and the duration of free coasting about five. On a small scale, the V-2 was indeed the prototype of the interplanetary spaceship, which must blast off from earth for about 10 minutes along a carefully calculated flight path, then coast effortlessly, with only minor flight corrections, for many months before it reaches the planet of destination.

Price of success

The first successful V-2 flight, which broke all records for height, weight, speed and range, took place at Peenemünde on October 3, 1942. Not until two years later, however, was the weapon ready for operational use, and it was then too late to change the outcome of the war. From the German point of view, the V-2 was a technological triumph but a military waste of time. Had the same effort gone into the production of rocket antiaircraft missiles, for example, the Allies might have been denied the skies of Europe. On the other hand, of course, if D-Day had then been made impossible, the first atomic bomb might have been dropped on Berlin, not Hiroshima. So perhaps, after all, Germany may well be thankful for the V-2.

There were those, even during the war, who suspected that Dr. Von Braun was slightly more interested in the conquest of space than the establishment of the Thousand-Year Reich. In March 1944, with two of his colleagues, he was suddenly arrested. He was held for two weeks having stated—to quote his own words—"that the V-2 was not intended as a weapon of war, that I had space travel in mind when it was developed, and that I regretted its imminent operational use." Von Braun's arrest was actually part of a plot by Himmler's organization to get control of Peenemünde. However, the SS had failed to reckon with the redoubtable Walter Dornberger, by then a general. He got the three engineers released by asserting that the V-2 would have *no* operational use, imminent or otherwise, without them.

The V-2's psychological triumph

In the history of space flight, the V-2 represented not only a tremendous technological breakthrough, but an equally important psychological one. Although its accomplishments had been substantially outlined by the pioneers of rocketry in their books and papers, it proved beyond all further argument that their basic theories were correct. The non-scientific public is seldom convinced by equations and graphs, though it may be confused by them, but no one could fail to be impressed by a 47-foot-high missile that climbed to the edge of space and drove a one-ton payload at 3,600 miles an hour.

After 1945, therefore, discussions of space travel were listened to with respect, and it was no longer necessary to explain at great length to skeptical critics that a rocket engine could continue to provide thrust in the vacuum beyond the atmosphere. A whole generation of space-flight enthusiasts had had to wrestle with the popular fallacy that a rocket worked by "pushing on the air behind it"; this misunderstanding had been extremely difficult to uproot because it seemed to have a perfectly logical basis. Those who advanced it felt that a rocket exhaust must have something to push against, and they were absolutely right. They simply missed the point that the exhaust gases pushed against the inside walls of the rocket chamber itself, and that what happened to them after they had left the nozzle was unimportant; the recoil of a gun is based on precisely the same principle.

Even those who appreciated this often found it hard to understand how a mere jet of gas could provide the 28 tons of thrust necessary to drive the V-2 upward, faster than a falling body accelerates downward. However, anyone who has ever attempted to walk into the teeth of a hurricane will agree that a moving gas—which is all that wind is—can exert appreciable force. By official definition, hurricane winds have a velocity of over 74 miles an hour. The velocity of the gas in a V-2 jet was 4,500 miles an hour—60 times as great.

The jet speed, or exhaust velocity, is the most important single factor affecting the performance of a rocket, and every effort is made to maximize it by using the most energetic fuels and the most efficient engines. However, there is only limited room for improvement—at least as long as chemical propellants are employed.

Since the V-2 there have been many experiments with new propellants and oxidizers. Lox, being extremely cheap, nonpoisonous and available in almost unlimited quantities, is such an ideal oxidizer that it has been challenged only in certain very special applications. Military men, who dislike its eagerness to boil away and to freeze everything in the neighborhood, have developed various oxygen-rich chemicals which are liquid at normal temperatures, and which support combustion almost as vigorously as does pure oxygen. (The Titan II rocket used such an oxidizer—nitrogen tetroxide.) For missions requiring the utmost in performance, scientists have selected an element which paradoxically is a better oxidizer than oxygen itself. This is the extremely reactive gas, fluorine, which combines with almost everything—including such unlikely substances as glass and most metals.

Although there are only a few practical oxidizers—oxygen itself, a handful of nitrogen-oxygen compounds, fluorine—the choice of fuels to burn with them is almost infinite. The alcohol of the V-2 soon gave way to various types of kerosene, similar to those used in jet engines. Kerosene fuels powered almost all the large space rockets of the early space age, but for the more difficult missions scheduled to follow, rocket men focused their attention on what has been called the ultimate fuel: hydrogen. Few substances give more energy per pound when they burn.

As a fuel, hydrogen might have been deliberately contrived to tantalize and frustrate the rocket engineer. It becomes liquid at an even lower temperature than oxygen—an unimaginable 420° below zero Fahrenheit. Until quite recently, it was out of the question to handle tons of liquid at such extremely low temperatures.

To aggravate the problem of storage, liquid hydrogen is extremely light and, therefore, bulky. It occupies 14 times the space of the same weight of water, so the fuel tanks of a hydrogen rocket have to be excessively large. For these reasons, although hydrogen has been recognized as the last word in rocket fuel for more than half a century, it was not until 1963 that a hydrogen-fueled rocket (Centaur) went into orbit, just 21 years after the flight of the first V-2.

A need for greater speed

Even using the old fuels, by 1960 the exhaust velocity attainable had climbed from the V-2's 4,500 mph to about 6,000 mph. With hydrogen the outer limit is around 8,000 mph. But 8,000 mph is a modest speed to set beside the velocities needed for interplanetary flight. To remain in orbit close to the earth, a satellite has to travel at 18,000 mph; to escape from the earth completely, a speed of 25,000 mph has to be achieved. Thus even the simplest one-way space missions involve speeds three or more times greater than those that can be attained by any rocket ex-

THE OLD-FASHIONED ROCKET

Rockets have been propelled by combustion motors ever since the 13th Century. Such rockets operate by burning fuel and an oxidizer in a combustion chamber. Expanding gases generated in the process escape through a nozzle and the rocket is driven forward. But the enormous fuel requirements limit the payload that can be carried.

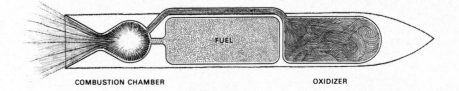

COMBUSTION CHAMBER   FUEL   OXIDIZER

haust. The very possibility of space flight, therefore, has from the start hinged on the answer to this question: Can one build a rocket that will fly faster than its own exhaust gases?

Tsiolkovsky had asked this fundamental question by the end of the 19th Century, and had derived the equation that gave the answer. Rather surprisingly, it turns out that up to the speed of light, there is no limit to the speed a rocket can attain; it depends upon the ingenuity of the designers in cutting down deadweight and packing in fuel. The mathematics show that to have any worthwhile performance at all, a rocket must consist of at least 75 per cent fuel by weight.

This is a striking contrast to all other vehicles. In an automobile, a locomotive or a ship, the weight of the fuel is almost negligible—usually no more than a few per cent of the total. Only in aircraft is the proportion appreciably higher; more than 50 per cent of the takeoff weight of a modern military jet is fuel.

The paradox: more fuel than rocket

Building such a vehicle, which weighs twice as much when fueled as when empty, represents a remarkable engineering achievement. Yet it is not good enough for a rocket. Even the now-primitive V-2 carried twice its empty weight in propellants (that is, it weighed three times as much when its tanks were full as when they were empty). Typical figures were: loaded weight 14 tons, empty weight four and a half tons. This 3-to-1 ratio is just sufficient to allow a rocket to fly as fast as its own jet; the V-2 did not achieve this, owing to air resistance and other losses, but could have done so easily if it were launched in empty space.

For a rocket to attain twice the speed of its exhaust, a 7-to-1 ratio of full-to-empty weight is necessary. Thus for the V-2 to have reached 9,000 mph, it would have been necessary to redesign its structure to hold 27 tons of propellant, instead of just under 10. This would have been an engineering impossibility—and even if it could have been built, the existing V-2 motor, with its 28-ton thrust, would not have been able to lift the resulting 31½-ton rocket off the launching pad.

Yet today, such fantastic ratios have been achieved, by brilliant design techniques and the use of new materials. The liquid-fueled Atlas rocket is virtually a metal balloon, with payload at one end and engine at the other. The tanks are so thin-walled that they cannot even stand up under their own weight, but have to be stiffened by internal pressurization, without which they would crumple and collapse.

Nature's nearest analogy to the fuel tanks of a modern rocket is an egg which weighs about 20 times as much full as empty. Some solid-propellant rockets (which do not have the weight penalty imposed by fuel pumps and their plumbing) had attained this figure by the 1960s.

THE NEW-FANGLED ROCKET
Space scientists are looking to nuclear energy to power the rockets of the future. Instead of being burned, the propellant gases may be heated by fissionable material in a reactor. The great advantage of nuclear propulsion is that it provides more efficient use of the propellant, meaning that less fuel will be required for longer voyages into space.

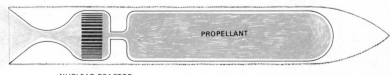

NUCLEAR REACTOR

PROPELLANT

Sooner or later, however, one comes to a point when no further improvement can be achieved—when, in the words of old-time aeronautical engineers, no more "lightness can be added." It is then necessary to try another approach. And in rocketry that approach is the step, or multistage, rocket.

The idea of mounting one rocket on top of another, piggyback fashion, originated 300 years ago in the writings of a fireworks maker named Johann Schmidlap. If each rocket in such an arrangement contributes its boost to the one above it and then drops off, very high final velocities may be achieved by the last rocket in the series. This technique of staging is vital to all space-flight plans, but it is a very expensive way of overcoming the feebleness of rocket propellants. A multistage vehicle at takeoff may weigh 1,000 times as much as its final payload.

At Peenemünde, plans had been made to give the V-2 transatlantic range by mounting it on a large booster, and several multistage solid-fueled rockets had been successfully flown. When Germany collapsed in the spring of 1945, all this information—all this vast background of theory and experience, acquired during a decade of secret research at a cost of millions of dollars—fell into the hands of the victorious Allies.

The key to the universe lay waiting for the nation that had the courage to pick it up.

Seven Centuries of the Rockets' Red Glare

Rockets have existed for at least 700 years. In the 13th Century the Chinese shot off the first recorded "fire arrows" and terrified invading Mongols. By the time of the Renaissance a century or so later, Europe had learned the principle —and its applications: one imaginative Italian designed a rocket-propelled battering ram to knock down enemy walls. Although the rocket ram was never used, rockets did prove effective in naval battles as a means of setting fire to ships' tarred rigging. By the late 18th Century, the British were building rockets somewhat like those opposite for fireworks and military uses. They were employed in the attack on Fort McHenry near Baltimore in 1814, producing the "rockets' red glare" that was immortalized in "The Star-Spangled Banner." The rockets of past centuries and those now whizzing around in space are based on precisely the same principles; the only difference is in technological sophistication.

SOME ANCESTRAL BOOSTERS
These rockets, all of which date back to the 1700s or earlier, demonstrate the early application of a number of vital principles employed in modern rocketry. The firecracker model *(left)* and the explosive rocket *(center)* are just noisemakers. But the other three utilize effects—multistages, stabilizing vanes, rocket clusters—that are an integral part of present or planned space vehicles.

THREE-STAGE ROCKET

EXPLOSIVE PAYLOAD

CLUSTERED ROCKETS

FIRECRACKER PAYLOAD

FIN-STABILIZED ROCKET

L. Hess

Made in America: The Goddard Rocket

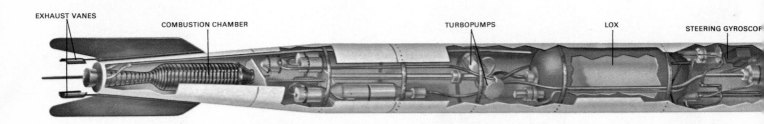

EXHAUST VANES COMBUSTION CHAMBER TURBOPUMPS LOX STEERING GYROSCOPE

Turbine-driven pumps forced fuel and lox into the Goddard rocket's combustion chamber. The greatest thrust recorded by this model was 985 pounds; it attained a height of only 300 feet.

Lox was carried aft of the rocket's fuel tanks. As the vehicle used up its propellant, nitrogen fiiled the tanks; the pressure of the gas helped maintain both structural strength and fuel flow.

Pride of Germany: The V-2 Rocket

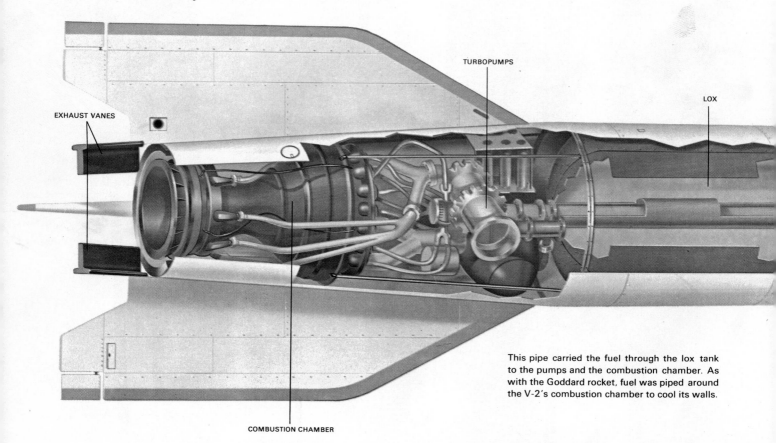

TURBOPUMPS LOX

EXHAUST VANES

This pipe carried the fuel through the lox tank to the pumps and the combustion chamber. As with the Goddard rocket, fuel was piped around the V-2's combustion chamber to cool its walls.

COMBUSTION CHAMBER

Space Sisters Born an Ocean Apart

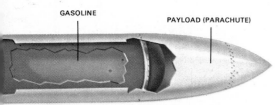

GASOLINE   PAYLOAD (PARACHUTE)

The fuel used by this missile was gasoline. It had a gyroscopic guidance mechanism *(red)*; the course could not be altered once set. The nose cone contained a parachute for recovery.

For centuries the rocket was mainly a curiosity, of little practical value to anyone. Then suddenly modern technology turned it into a major tool of both warfare and science.

There is a saying among scientists that when the time is ripe for a breakthrough, advances seem to occur independently and simultaneously. In rocketry the vital step was taken by Robert H. Goddard in the United States and by a scientific team in Germany; separated by an ocean and a wartime wall of secrecy, they developed almost identical rocket designs. The Goddard rocket shown here was built in 1941; the German V-2 made its first successful flight in 1942. At 46 feet, the V-2 was almost twice the other's length (the drawings on these pages are not to scale); and it carried 18,700 pounds of fuel and liquid oxygen (lox) as against 252 for the Goddard model. But the essentials were remarkably similar. Dr. Walter R. Dornberger, chief of the German V-2 team, has said simply: "That was the only way to build a rocket."

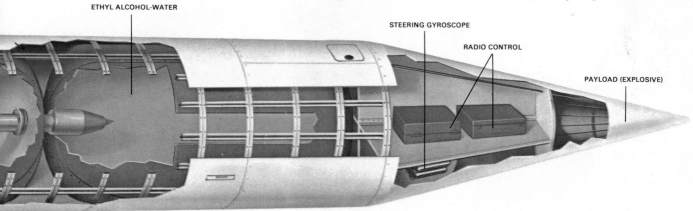

ETHYL ALCOHOL-WATER   STEERING GYROSCOPE   RADIO CONTROL   PAYLOAD (EXPLOSIVE)

The first V-2 was fueled by a mixture of ethyl alcohol and water. The water reduced the rocket's velocity somewhat, but without it the engine temperature would have been too high.

As with the Goddard rocket, the V-2's steering was by gyroscopes which activated movable exhaust vanes. In certain experimental models, the rocket's fuel supply could be cut off by radio.

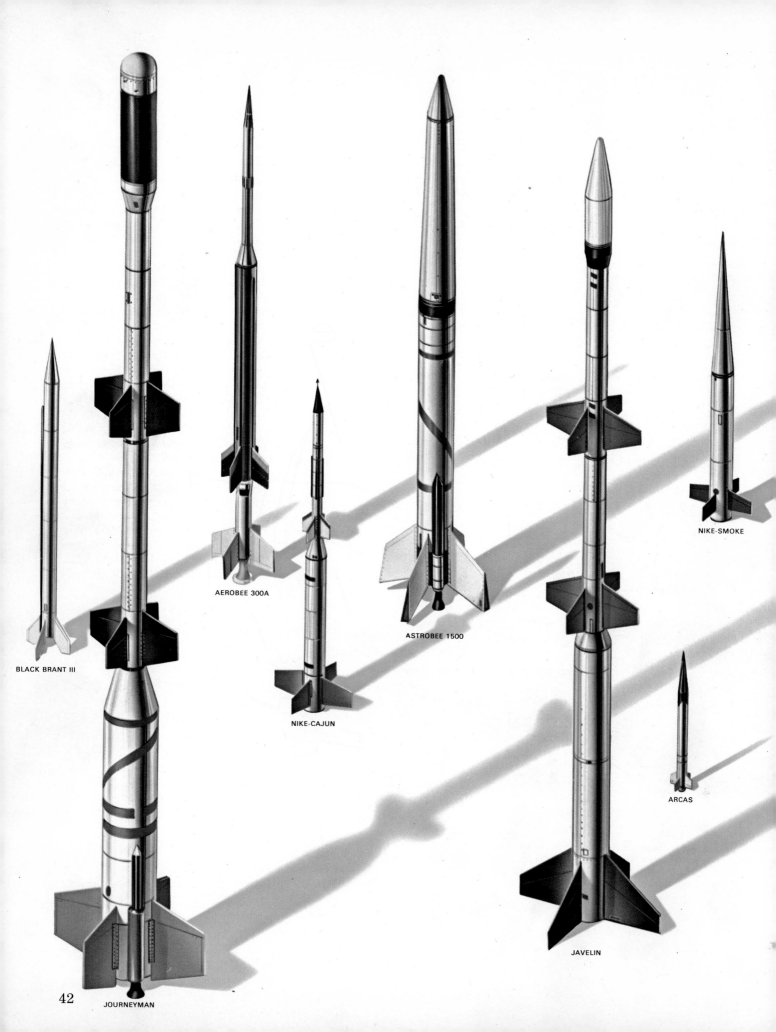

BLACK BRANT III

JOURNEYMAN

AEROBEE 300A

NIKE-CAJUN

ASTROBEE 1500

JAVELIN

NIKE-SMOKE

ARCAS

42

Taking a Sample of Space

In the same way that a sailor tests the depth of his ship's channel with a sounding line, scientists explore the reaches of the earth's upper atmosphere with sounding rockets. Their function is to sample a small area in space and provide an immediate report. The data that they may gather are usually returned to earth by parachute or radio (though one sounding rocket, the Nike-Smoke, emits a vapor that is photographed from the ground). This information provides scientists with a new understanding of such matters as cosmic rays, the chemical composition of the upper atmosphere, the prevalence of micrometeorites and the nature of the earth's magnetic field. The probes also help engineers to anticipate the problems of manned space flight and to test new instruments for satellites.

The first U.S. sounding rocket—a WAC Corporal—was fired at White Sands, New Mexico, in 1945. Since then a number of different kinds of rockets *(opposite)* have been used for different experiments, providing a chance to try out many new designs and making an important contribution toward putting man into space.

A STABLE OF SOUNDING ROCKETS
The eight sounding rockets opposite show the variety of these projectiles—from the eight-foot, $1,800 Arcas to the 62-foot, $150,000 Journeyman. All are solid-fueled except the solid-plus-liquid Aerobee 300A. The Black Brant III is Canadian; the others are U.S. designs. The smaller ones are most often used, since they require the least elaborate ground installations.

SPANNING THE UPPER ATMOSPHERE
This graph suggests how the various sounding rockets enable scientists to study conditions at many altitudes. The height reached by a particular rocket depends upon such variables as its payload and the angle of firing. The figures given here in statute miles are the heights reached by rockets carrying the payloads noted. The altitudes on the chart are not drawn to scale.

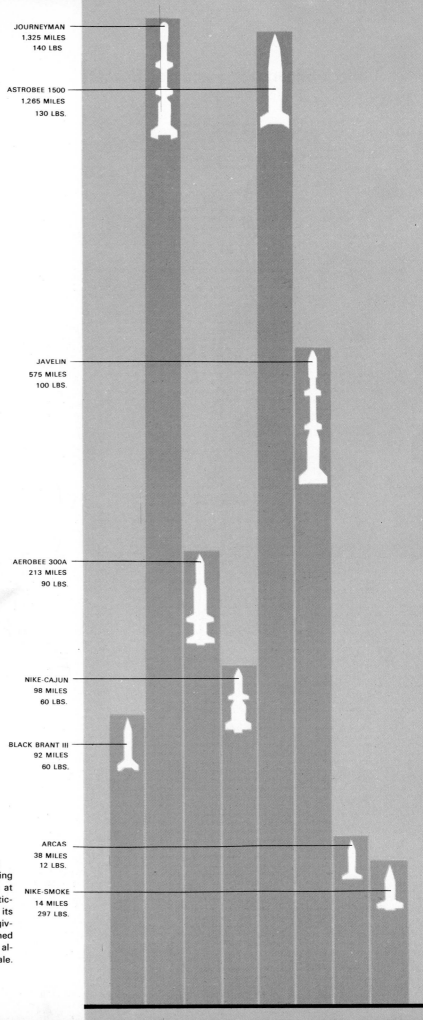

JOURNEYMAN
1,325 MILES
140 LBS

ASTROBEE 1500
1,265 MILES
130 LBS.

JAVELIN
575 MILES
100 LBS.

AEROBEE 300A
213 MILES
90 LBS.

NIKE-CAJUN
98 MILES
60 LBS.

BLACK BRANT III
92 MILES
60 LBS.

ARCAS
38 MILES
12 LBS.

NIKE-SMOKE
14 MILES
297 LBS.

A Three-Generation Family of Rockets

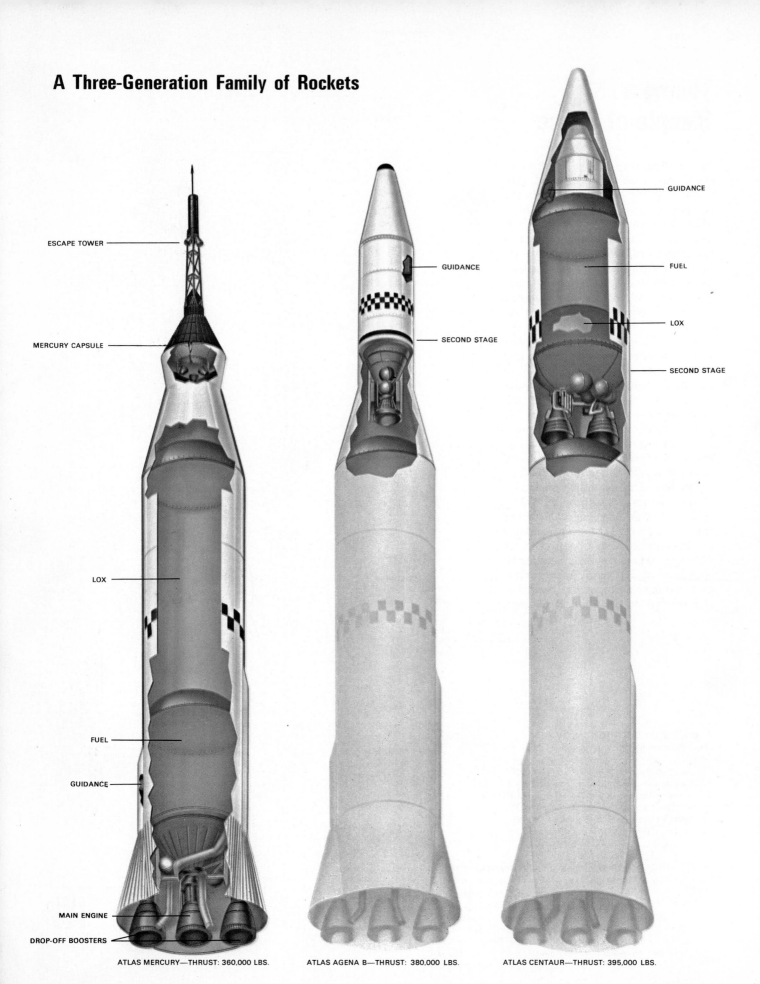

ESCAPE TOWER

MERCURY CAPSULE

GUIDANCE

GUIDANCE

SECOND STAGE

FUEL

LOX

SECOND STAGE

LOX

FUEL

GUIDANCE

MAIN ENGINE

DROP-OFF BOOSTERS

ATLAS MERCURY—THRUST: 360,000 LBS.   ATLAS AGENA B—THRUST: 380,000 LBS.   ATLAS CENTAUR—THRUST: 395,000 LBS.

44

Building Up to Greater Power

The more ambitious the mission of a rocket, the more efficient its power plant must be. Thrust is what gets it off the ground, into orbit, or free of earth's gravity for a voyage across space. With each increase in thrust, there is a bonus in increased payload weight—whether instruments or men and supplies.

The search for more powerful fuels has turned up many kinds, but all have one thing in common: they must be provided with an oxidizer to permit combustion outside the atmosphere. There are three main types at present: (1) ordinary liquid, usually a kerosenelike hydrocarbon—it requires a separate oxidizer, such as liquid oxygen; (2) solid, such as a nitroglycerin-nitrocellulose combination that contains a source of oxygen within itself; (3) high-energy liquid, a liquid hydrogen fuel that is about one third again as powerful as the best hydrocarbon. Adding liquid fluorine to the lox (flox) increases this power still further. The rockets on these pages are color-keyed to show the propellants they use: green for liquid fuel; rust for solid, blue for the oxidizer.

THE ATLAS AND HOW IT GREW
These versions of the Atlas show how components are combined for greater power. The Atlas Mercury at far left is essentially a 72-foot ICBM topped by an astronaut's capsule. The Atlas Agena B is the same rocket; on it is mounted a second engine, restartable in space. The Atlas Centaur adds a more powerful second stage, boosted by the first U.S. liquid-hydrogen engine.

A SOLID BOOST FOR LIQUID FUELS
The core of the 199-foot Titan IIIC (far right) is liquid-fueled, but it has solid-fueled strap-on boosters; providing extra initial thrust, they drop off. Without boosters, as the two-stage Titan II, it serves as an ICBM. The 90-foot Thor Delta Vehicle uses liquid fuel in its first two stages and solid in the third. Among others, it has orbited Telstar and Echo satellites.

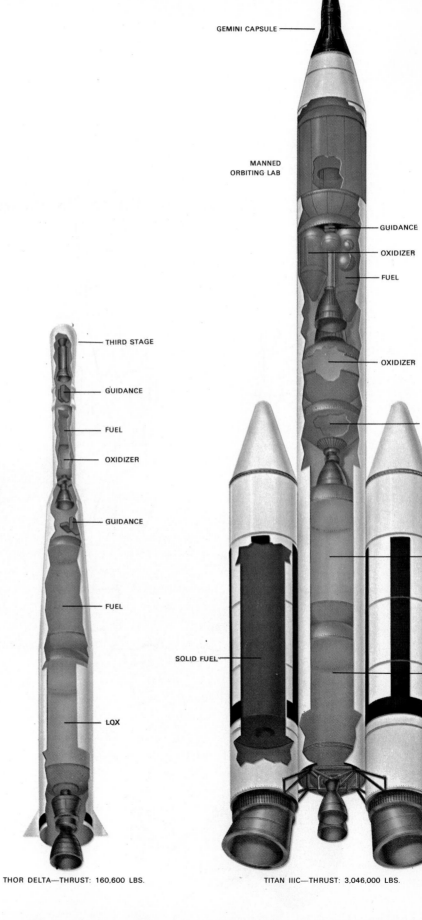

THOR DELTA—THRUST: 160,600 LBS.

TITAN IIIC—THRUST: 3,046,000 LBS.

45

A Space Cruiser 35 Stories High

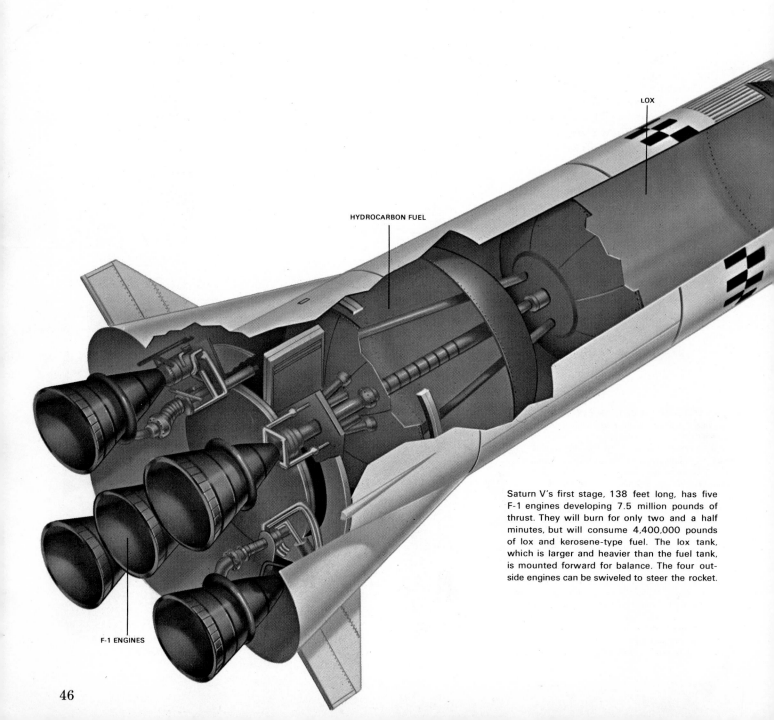

LOX

HYDROCARBON FUEL

F-1 ENGINES

Saturn V's first stage, 138 feet long, has five F-1 engines developing 7.5 million pounds of thrust. They will burn for only two and a half minutes, but will consume 4,400,000 pounds of lox and kerosene-type fuel. The lox tank, which is larger and heavier than the fuel tank, is mounted forward for balance. The four outside engines can be swiveled to steer the rocket.

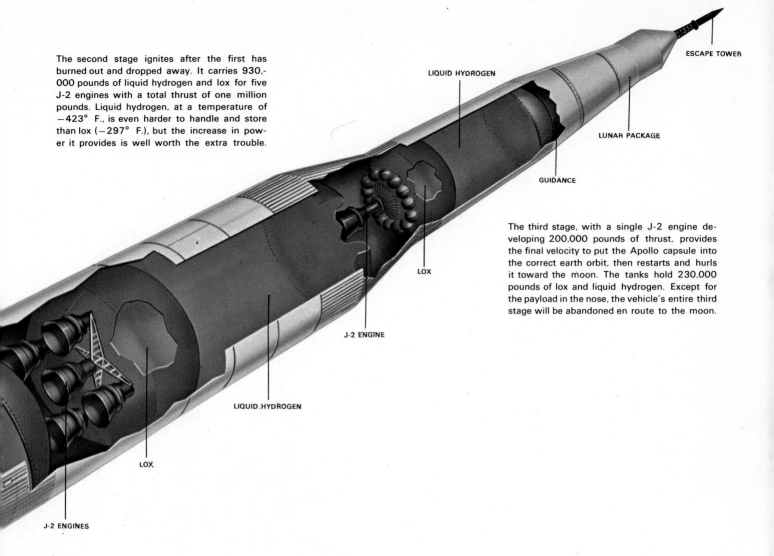

The second stage ignites after the first has burned out and dropped away. It carries 930,000 pounds of liquid hydrogen and lox for five J-2 engines with a total thrust of one million pounds. Liquid hydrogen, at a temperature of −423° F., is even harder to handle and store than lox (−297° F.), but the increase in power it provides is well worth the extra trouble.

LIQUID HYDROGEN

ESCAPE TOWER

LUNAR PACKAGE

GUIDANCE

LOX

J-2 ENGINE

LIQUID HYDROGEN

LOX

J-2 ENGINES

The third stage, with a single J-2 engine developing 200,000 pounds of thrust, provides the final velocity to put the Apollo capsule into the correct earth orbit, then restarts and hurls it toward the moon. The tanks hold 230,000 pounds of lox and liquid hydrogen. Except for the payload in the nose, the vehicle's entire third stage will be abandoned en route to the moon.

A Giant Rocket, a Mighty Mission

The big rocket on these pages is the Saturn V, which was designed to carry the Apollo astronauts to the moon. Its statistics are as awesome as its mission. It is 360 feet tall—higher than a 35-story building. At lift-off, it weighs more than 3,000 tons. To get it off the ground, the first-stage engine must develop 20 times the thrust of the mighty Atlas-Mercury. Most of the rocket's initial weight is for propellants; their final job is to accelerate a 45-ton payload to a speed of 25,000 miles an hour.

No such machine could be built from scratch. The Saturn V is the culmination of an evolutionary process

that began in 1958. First came the Saturn I, which by early 1964 had placed unmanned Apollo capsules in orbit. Saturn I provided a test of a liquid-hydrogen-and-lox fuel combination. Next in the evolutionary series came the Saturn IB, with thrust enough to place manned Apollo capsules into low earth orbit for training missions. Saturn V is the last, most powerful member of the family.

Despite Saturn V's advanced design, experts are already seeking to improve it. One proposal is to substitute clusters of solid-fuel motors for the liquid-fueled first stage, thereby increasing the payload by 10 per cent.

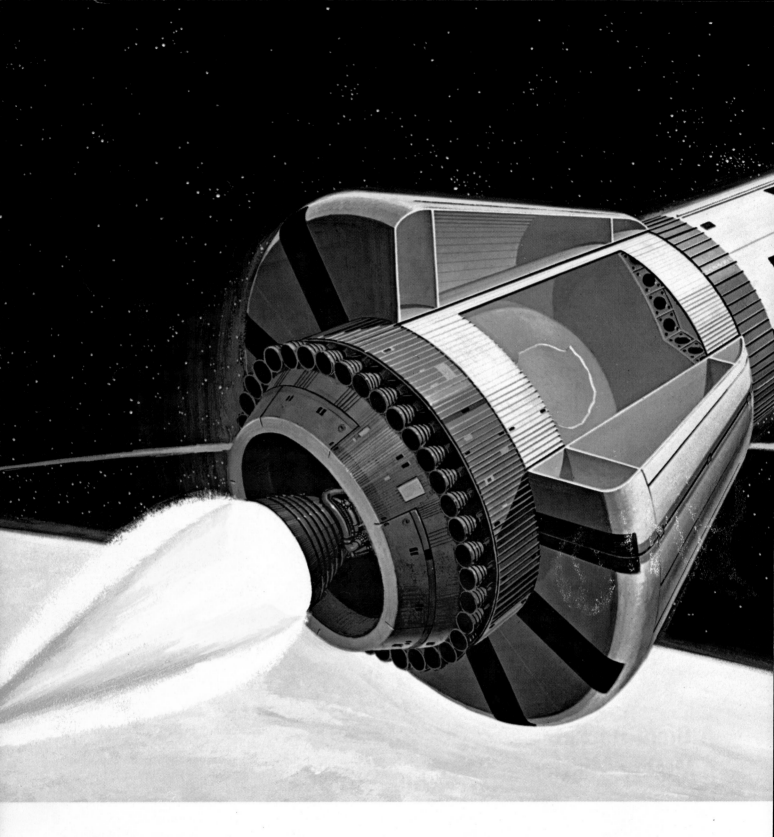

Proposed Monsters of Outer Space

Even bigger rockets will follow Saturn V. A dozen or more designs, with the generic name of Nova, are under consideration. The drawing above shows two possibilities. The big rocket in the foreground, about 400 feet long, would be able to put a 500-ton payload into orbit. Loaded, it would weigh more than 10,000 tons. The rocket in the rear is basically a Saturn V body with improved engines and strap-on solid-fuel boosters.

Rockets the size of the Novas pose an entirely new set of problems. They are so expensive that parts of them will have to be recovered from space by parachute if the space program is not to go broke. They are so noisy

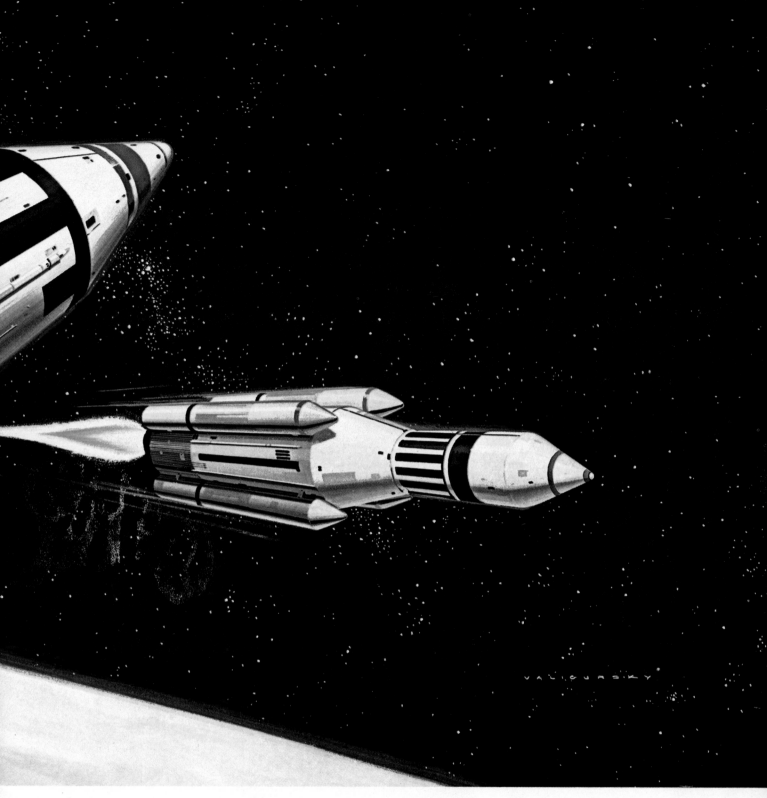

(and a takeoff explosion would create such a hazard) that some scientists believe no unprotected human could safely stand within 14 miles of the launching site. Novas may have to be launched from offshore bases similar to Texas towers, after being towed out in sections and assembled at sea. And that will just add to the expense.

LINKS WITH THE PLANETS
The Nova rockets, like these, could lift sections of an interplanetary spaceship into orbit. There the craft would be assembled and launched on a voyage to, say, Mars. They could also serve for trips to the moon, or in the construction of space platforms as sites for scientific laboratories.

A Twinned Vehicle That Halves Costs

The ultimate in the recoverable booster would be one that could be guided back to earth completely intact after serving its purpose in space. One such concept is the "Siamese Twin" craft shown here. The two ships in the foreground are actually the separating halves of a single vehicle. They were joined at takeoff. Now, at a speed six times that of sound, the first stage breaks away to return to earth while its twin begins to build up speed for entry into orbit. Later, the second stage too will return to earth for a runway landing.

Several versions of this craft are being studied; the one shown here, instead of being powered by rockets, is pushed along by jets. Since jets must have air, the second stage must achieve top speed while still in the atmosphere; only then can it hurtle into space. Once in orbit, it uses small rockets for maneuvering.

By doing away with the wasteful expenditure of boosters, vehicles such as this one can bring about a sharp reduction in space costs. One estimate is that the cost of carrying equipment into orbit might be cut by as much as 95 per cent—to about $50 a pound.

AIRPLANES IN SPACE
The two halves of a Siamese Twin orbital ship break apart while another vehicle, in the distance, is shown before separation. These craft are airplanes in every sense of the word. They take off normally, are guided through the atmosphere by human pilots, and land on runways.

3

A Long
Interlude
in the U.S.

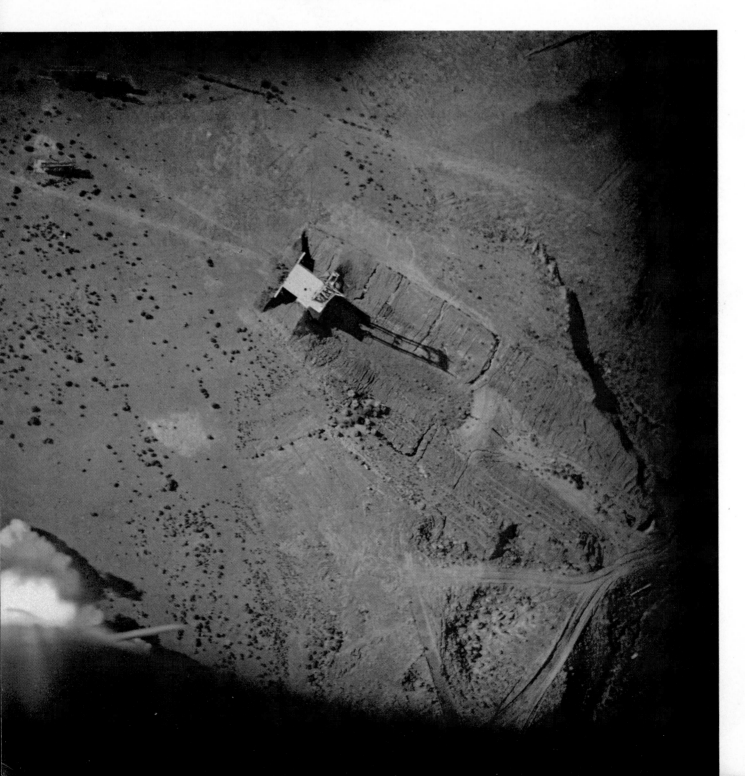

"This is absolutely intolerable. We defeated the Nazi armies; we occupied Berlin and Peenemünde—but the Americans got the rocket engineers. What could be more revolting and inexcusable? How and why was this allowed to happen?"

—JOSEPH STALIN TO GENERAL I. A. SEROV

ON SEPTEMBER 20, 1956, about a year before Sputnik I went into orbit, a rocket rose from Cape Canaveral and arced out over the Atlantic. The United States Army rocket functioned perfectly, the last stage reaching a speed never before approached by any man-made object—13,000 miles an hour. Another 5,000 miles an hour and it would have gone into orbit.

This rocket could easily have achieved orbital speed; the reason it did not was as simple as it is hard to believe. The Department of Defense, suspecting (not without reason) that the Army might launch an unauthorized satellite and apologize later, had ordered that the last stage must be an empty dummy; Dr. Wernher Von Braun was personally directed to make sure that this order was obeyed. Not until 16 months later—when two Russian satellites had already orbited—was he given an opportunity to launch an almost identical vehicle with a live final stage. That final stage was the first United States satellite, Explorer I.

In the eyes of the public, America had lost the space race; the resulting national humiliation threatened to dominate the entire international scene in the late 1950s. The circumstances leading up to this situation have been largely concealed by a smokescreen of excuses, countercharges and half-truths, as well as by that very human trait, the refusal to face unpleasant facts. But here is what actually occurred, so far as the events of the dozen years from the end of World War II to the launching of Sputnik I can be condensed into a few pages.

With the collapse of Germany in May 1945, the Russian armies captured Peenemünde, the Baltic island where the Germans had developed the V-2. The Soviets derived few benefits from Peenemünde, however. Some months earlier the installations there had been largely destroyed, and later the scientists and engineers had been evacuated by the Germans. Before leaving, Von Braun and all but one of his most senior men agreed to surrender to the Americans when the opportunity arose.

The Americans on their part were prepared to welcome such a surrender. Two months before, the Pentagon had established "Operation Paperclip," whose purpose was to recruit top German scientists to work in the U.S. But at the time of Von Braun's decision, surrendering was no simple matter. Germany was in a state of chaos, and die-hard SS troops were likely to liquidate any German who lacked enthusiasm for a last-ditch stand against the Allies.

A HATCHERY FOR AN EARLY BIRD
An outbound Aerobee Hi sounding rocket took this 1958 picture of its launching pad at White Sands Missile Range, the U.S. Government's first rocket proving ground. From here some 65 captured German V-2 rockets were fired. One of them carried an American-built WAC Corporal rocket that soared 250 miles high and gave man his first real glimpse of outer space.

But finally, on May 2, Von Braun's young brother Magnus ("I was the youngest, I spoke the best English, and I was the most expendable") bicycled his way into the American lines. He was met by Pfc. Fred P. Schneiker of Sheboygan, Wisconsin, a soldier in the 44th Division. Schneiker had never heard of either Operation Paperclip or Wernher von Braun; he took Magnus to Counter Intelligence Corps Headquarters. The officer in charge there appeared equally at a loss. He dismissed Magnus, saying skeptically that if in fact he did have a cache of scientists up in the hills, he should bring them in the following day.

Thus, almost in spite of themselves, the Americans acquired one of the most valuable prizes of World War II. The haul ultimately included Walter Dornberger, Von Braun, about 120 of the top V-2 planners, scientists and engineers, and more than a ton of secret documents.

300 freight cars of rockets

Meanwhile a special U.S. Army unit under Colonel Holger N. Toftoy had been established to find out everything possible about the German V-2 program—and some quick thinking by this group provided the United States with the hardware to go with the German scientists and their documents. Under the Potsdam agreement, Nordhausen, in the Harz Mountains, lay in an area due to be handed over to the Russians for occupation. It was also stipulated at Potsdam that no German plants were to be stripped by the victors. But Nordhausen happened to be the site of a V-2 factory, and Toftoy's men could not be concerned with diplomatic niceties. A small team from the Ordnance Corps moved into the factory, and 300 freight cars full of V-2 parts moved out. The chief rocket scientist of the Soviet Air Force complained later: "The underground factory of V-2 rockets in the Harz Mountains was captured by the U.S. Army, quickly dismantled, and sent, together with its staff, to the United States. Nothing was left behind. . . . The U.S.S.R. did not get a single leading V-2 rocket engineer or administrator."

For a time it seemed that the United States was about to take full advantage of the lead in rocketry it had achieved by the "capture" of the Peenemünde team and its secrets and equipment. The Navy and the Army Air Force inaugurated separate secret studies of the potentialities of space research. With great foresight both of these studies concluded that a program to put up satellites was feasible and desirable.

The Air Force study had begun even before the end of World War II, when Commanding General Henry ("Hap") Arnold asked Dr. Theodore von Kármán, an eminent aerodynamicist, to investigate the postwar role of the air arm. Von Kármán's findings were published in a voluminous report, the gist of which was that the missile was the weapon of the future, and that satellites in orbit around the earth were practical in view of the great advance in rocketry demonstrated by the German V-2.

In 1945 the Navy did its own study of space rocketry; its investigators recommended that development of an earth satellite should be undertaken immediately. Cost of the program was estimated at five to eight million dollars. Accordingly the Navy awarded a research contract to the Guggenheim Aeronautical Laboratory at Caltech. All this took place under the tightest security.

A few months later, Project RAND (Research and Development), at the behest of the Army Air Force, submitted the most forward-looking and prophetic report of all—again in secret.

"Although the crystal ball is cloudy," the report said, "two things seem clear—

"1. A satellite vehicle with appropriate instrumentation can be expected to be one of the most potent scientific tools of the Twentieth Century.

"2. The achievement of a satellite craft by the United States would inflame the imagination of mankind, and would probably produce repercussions in the world comparable to the explosion of the atomic bomb. . . .

"Since mastery of the elements is a reliable index of material progress, the nation which first makes significant achievements in space travel will be acknowledged as the world leader in both military and scientific techniques. To visualize the impact on the world, one can imagine the consternation and admiration that would be felt here if the U.S. were to discover suddenly that some other nation had already put up a successful satellite."

An electrifying announcement

At this point, there were two military space programs. Twice there were Army-Navy meetings aimed at pooling resources; in the atmosphere of interservice rivalry existing in the late 1940s no agreement was possible. If anything, the conferences left the participants even further apart.

Then suddenly, in 1948, Secretary of Defense James T. Forrestal dropped a bombshell. He announced publicly that an earth-satellite program was under way. The whole world was electrified. The Russians called Forrestal a "madman" and said he was working on an "instrument of blackmail." But the armed forces were stunned at the public disclosure of their secret programs—and they were even more appalled at another feature of the Forrestal announcement. Henceforward, he declared, the military space effort would be administered by a single authority—and it would be confined merely to "studies and component designs."

While the public was still trying to get used to the idea of a space program, military rocket advocates—forbidden to build new missiles—knew that the space program was, to all purposes, dead.

There were a number of reasons for Forrestal's action. There was grave doubt as to the military usefulness of rockets in the atomic age. The RAND report, while urging a satellite program, had also said that the existing atomic bomb probably was too big to be delivered to any distant target by any conceivable rocket. A special committee appointed by Forrestal under Dr. Clark Millikan of Caltech had borne out this view. Funds for the military had been cut back sharply during the postwar era; it was doubtful that Congress would appropriate any substantial money for a nonmilitary space effort.

It was known that the Russians had a rocket program. But, as the Army rocket expert, General John B. Medaris, later said, "it was fashionable to think of them as retarded folk who depended mainly on a few captured German scientists for their achievements, if any. And since the cream of the German planners had surrendered to the Americans, so the argument ran, there was nothing to worry about."

Nevertheless, one small rocket program still existed. In test launchings at the newly established White Sands Proving Grounds in New Mexico, Wernher Von Braun and his colleagues were imparting to the Americans every intricacy of the V-2, using captured rockets.

Science takes a hand

Holger Toftoy, the officer whose men had spirited the V-2 parts away from the Russians, was now at White Sands supervising the rockets' reassembly. He realized that the V-2s might serve a dual purpose—not only as study rockets for future military missiles, but also to carry out scientific studies of the upper atmosphere. This was a highly acceptable proposal to the military men; the V-2 would not function anyhow without carrying a payload weighing at least a ton in the space provided for the warhead. Accordingly, the V-2 Upper Atmosphere Research Panel was inaugurated in January 1946, with Dr. James A. Van Allen as chairman to coordinate the scientific efforts.

At White Sands and elsewhere, about 70 captured or rebuilt V-2s were launched, and a great deal was learned about conditions in space. Equipment for tracking rockets and for radioing back information from them while they were in flight (telemetering) was developed or refined, and the foundations were laid for scientific space research. Many of the physicists whose names are now famous in this field—including Dr. William H. Pickering, Dr. Homer E. Newell and Dr. Fred L. Whipple—had their baptism of rocketry at White Sands.

Since the supply of V-2s was limited, a replacement rocket would have to be developed if scientific work was to continue. So the White

AN ARTIST'S SPACE STATION

This space platform was one artist's reaction to the Defense Department announcement in 1948 that work was progressing on an "earth satellite vehicle program." Much misinformation was circulated. Some said the vehicle would go into orbit at 10,000 mph —about half the necessary speed—while others reported plans for mysterious lethal rays. Within three years, scientists were publishing serious satellite suggestions (opposite).

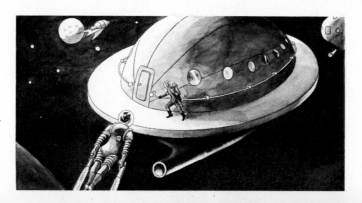

Sands scientists initiated a program to develop new high-altitude research rockets on their own. One of these was the Viking, a 48-foot rocket, designed specifically for scientific investigation. The White Sands scientists also made use of the Army's WAC Corporal, a product of World War II development. In 1949, one of these, mounted atop a captured V-2, set an altitude record of 250 miles which stood for seven years—until the near-orbital 682-mile flight of Von Braun's Jupiter-C in 1956.

Among the many experimental rocket techniques tried by the scientists who worked at White Sands was an adaptation of a proposal long discussed by rocket pioneers but never before tested. Van Allen now revived it. He proposed using a balloon to carry a rocket into the thin upper atmosphere, and launching the missile from there. A rocket so fired would be spared the difficult flight through the dense part of the atmosphere, and would therefore achieve much greater altitude. Van Allen assigned the name "rockoon" to this device. The technique worked extremely well, and rockets up to 13 feet long were launched in this fashion. In fact, it was so successful that for a time scientists seriously considered using balloons to carry large three-stage rockets aloft for the purpose of putting a satellite into orbit.

In this fashion, the purely scientific White Sands program contributed ideas to the science of rocketry that would later prove invaluable in the development of military missiles. The Aerobee rocket, designed strictly as an upper-air sounding device, later became the prototype for the Nike antiaircraft guided missile. The experience gained with a little-known sounding rocket, the MX-774, later proved vital in the development of the Atlas ICBM.

The research program at White Sands ranged over a wide assortment of experiments, including the composition of the atmosphere, the behavior of winds, solar radiation, the earth's magnetic field and cosmic radiation; they also photographed the earth from heights of over 100 miles.

A new life for the missile

In 1950 Von Braun was transferred from White Sands to Redstone Arsenal at Huntsville, Alabama. That June war broke out in Korea and suddenly the need for military rocketry appeared pressing. Within a month Von Braun was ordered to make a feasibility study for a 500-mile-range ballistic missile. His report was favorable, and work on the rocket was begun that autumn. A high priority was assigned to the project; the rocket was eventually christened the Redstone.

While Americans were building rockets, European scientists, lacking the funds for practical tests, were at work on the theoretical aspects of satellites and other projects in space. Even before World War II had ended, English space enthusiasts had revived the British Interplane-

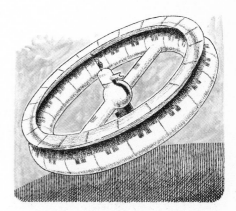

AN EXPERT'S SPACE STATION

This 250-foot space wheel could be orbited with 10 years' work for four billion dollars, space expert Wernher Von Braun said in 1952. Rocket ships would carry prefabricated parts into orbit where astronaut technicians would assemble them. When completed, the wheel would be spun to provide artificial gravity for the crew, living inside for lengthy periods. Many scientists feel it is still the most likely shape for a large space platform.

tary Society, originally started in 1933; under its sponsorship, the Second International Congress on Astronautics took place in September 1951 in London (the first had been held in Paris a year earlier). The theme of the London congress was "The Artificial Satellite," and among the papers read was a design study of satellites which could carry instruments into orbit. The incidental suggestion was made that one useful payload might be an inflatable, metallized balloon that could be tracked optically or by radar; less than 10 years later, the whole world was to watch precisely such an object—the brilliant, moving star of Echo I. From 1951 onward the idea of the instrument-carrying artificial satellite was, if one may use such an understatement, very much in the air.

One of those attending the London conference was a young physicist named Dr. Fred Singer, who was in London working for the U.S. Office of Naval Research. He had been associated with the launching of high-altitude rockets at White Sands. (The members of the British Interplanetary Society were very much impressed to meet someone who had seen V-2s going up; they had only experienced them coming down.)

An orbiting tape recorder

Because at White Sands he had participated in the development of instruments carried by research rockets, Dr. Singer could make realistic plans for future satellites, and he offered one of the first concrete proposals for satellite instrumentation. Among his designs was one for a 100-pound sphere, launched into an orbit that would carry it over the poles. On board would be a tape recorder, which would store up information and rebroadcast it on demand; here, in effect, was a prototype for the dozens of scientific satellites that the space age later spawned.

The best of ideas may fail to make an impact owing to poor publicity; the Singer satellite was launched into the world's press with alcohol fuel from the bar of London's famed Arts Theatre Club, off Leicester Square. It was here, one evening in 1953, that Dr. Singer, A. V. Cleaver —now chief engineer of the Rolls Royce Rocket Division—and I sat down with the deliberate intention of concocting a catchy name for the project. After some laboring, we brought forth MOUSE—Minimum Orbital Unmanned Satellite of Earth. We were as pleased as any advertising agency when the name caught on, and during the next two years the fame of MOUSE traveled all over the world. Singer's drawings were frequently reproduced, sometimes without acknowledgment, in the Russian press—with the result that, in the post-Sputnik period, they often came back to the West as examples of Russian satellite technology.

Meanwhile the first big public meeting on space had occurred in the United States. Willy Ley, who had helped found the German Society for Space Travel in 1927 and had been promoting astronautics for years in his many books and articles, persuaded New York's Hayden Planetarium to let him conduct a Space Flight Symposium. This took place, appropriately enough, on Columbus Day, October 12, 1951, and attracted a great deal of attention. Among other things, this symposium triggered a celebrated series of articles in *Collier's* magazine which gave Von Braun his first major opportunity to reach the American public at large with the message of the possible future in space.

Then, on November 1, 1952, independent of anything having to do with space, an event occurred which was to become perhaps the single most important influence on the U.S. space program. This was the development of the first American hydrogen device. In less than a year Russia, too, had set off a successful hydrogen explosion.

In the United States a committee was formed, headed by Dr. John Von Neumann, Hungarian-born mathematical genius, to review the entire subject of strategic missiles. Out of the work of this committee came two significant findings. The first was Von Neumann's hypothesis that a hydrogen weapon could be reduced sufficiently in size to be carried by a missile only slightly larger than the V-2. The second was that under the circumstances "the ballistic missile program—the ICBM—be accelerated to the maximum extent that technology would permit." Suddenly the rocket was back in action as a major military weapon. In 1954 the Atlas ICBM program, originally proposed eight years earlier, was revived.

It was now clear to everyone in the rocket business that the United States would soon possess at least a limited satellite-launching capability. A space flight subcommittee of the American Rocket Society submitted a report on space research to the National Science Foundation, in the hope that it would stimulate government action in this field. At about the same time, the Office of Naval Research started investigating, with Redstone Arsenal, the prospects for using a Redstone-solid-fuel rocket combination to launch a payload of about five pounds into orbit. This was Project Orbiter. Plans had been made for an Orbiter launch into an equatorial orbit in the summer of 1957—when the shadow of the approaching International Geophysical Year fell across the scene.

A competition among satellites

The U.S. National Committee on the IGY had recommended the launching of a small scientific satellite during the 18 months (July 1, 1957 to December 31, 1958) of this misnamed "year." The recommendation was accepted by the government, and on July 29, 1955, President Eisenhower made a new announcement of a U.S. satellite program. Which satellite, however, remained undecided.

The most ambitious proposal was made by the Air Force, which wanted to send up a large satellite using the new Atlas missile as the first

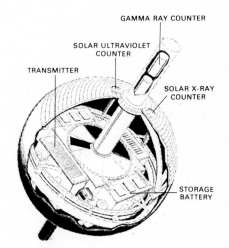

THE MOUSE THAT DID NOT FLY

Four years before Sputnik, when satellites orbited only in science fiction, a U.S. Navy physicist, Dr. Fred Singer, proposed a "Minimum Orbital Unmanned Satellite of the Earth" (MOUSE) in hopes of getting a bona fide space program under way. With the technology available in 1953, he said, the 100-pound satellite could be orbited for one million dollars—cheaper than the cost of a jet bomber. But MOUSE was never built.

stage and an Aerobee Hi rocket as the second. The Orbiter proposal, sponsored by Von Braun and his U.S. Army team, would have used a Redstone missile, surmounted by a cluster of small Loki rockets to serve as upper stages. Though the Orbiter payload would have allowed only for a five-pound satellite, its proponents argued that it would be simple, cheap and quick. Finally, there was the Navy's Project Vanguard. It would employ an advanced version of the Viking rocket developed at White Sands, with an Aerobee Hi rocket as second stage and a solid-fueled third stage. Vanguard would put into orbit a payload weighing about 20 pounds.

To decide between these rival proposals a high-powered scientific committee was set up under the chairmanship of Dr. Homer J. Stewart, one of the country's leading authorities on aerodynamics and rockets. It turned down the ambitious Air Force project on grounds that use of the still-untried Atlas might delay the vital ICBM program. The committee was then faced with the necessity of a choice between Orbiter and the more advanced vehicle proposed by the Navy. To the bitter disappointment of Von Braun and his team, the Navy was given the job.

A verdict for Vanguard

Few technical decisions have ever been more momentous, or more bitterly criticized. It was not a unanimous decision (Dr. Stewart himself strongly supported Orbiter), and even now it is a gross oversimplification to say that the committee's verdict was wrong. It gave the United States a brilliantly designed and highly efficient vehicle which eventually far exceeded its original specifications; even when the Vanguard program was ended, the individual stages developed for the rocket continued to play an essential role in the U.S. space program.

It was true, as later events showed, that the decision to go ahead with the more sophisticated Vanguard rather than the tried and tested Redstone ensured that the Russians would be first in space. Yet, whichever decision had been made, it would not have affected the real issue—the enormous lead that the Soviet Union enjoyed in space boosters. Even if the United States had been first to put a 10-pound payload into orbit, the shock produced by the appearance of a 1,000-pound Soviet satellite a few months later would still have been shattering, and the recriminations would still have been almost as great as they were in October 1957.

Although many details of the Soviet space effort may always remain hidden in secrecy, more is known in the West about early Russian space planning than is generally realized. As has been mentioned, no country has had a longer or more sustained interest in astronautics, and during the 1930s, there was a great deal of work in Russia on liquid-fuel rockets for high-altitude research and jet-assisted takeoff. But there was no attempt before the war to produce rockets on any such scale as the V-2.

"ROCKOONS" INTO ORBIT
In 1955 rocketeers suggested orbiting satellites by lifting them above the dense lower atmosphere with balloons—a method used in 1952 to launch small test rockets. The rockoon system could carry a 13,500-pound rocket to 15 miles before firing (below). The first stage would drive the package to 20 miles, the second to 200 and the third would put the 30-pound payload into orbit. The idea was dropped when better boosters were developed.

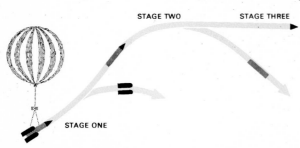

STAGE TWO   STAGE THREE

STAGE ONE

The Peenemünde revelations made a great impression on Stalin, and he decided that long-range rockets might give him an answer to the American A-bomb. So the Russians, a little belatedly, rounded up all the German rocket technicians they could find, together with such bits and pieces of V-2s as Colonel Toftoy's team had left behind, and shipped them to the U.S.S.R. Interestingly, the Germans working in Russia did not succeed in launching their first V-2 until the fall of 1947; by that time almost 30 had been fired at White Sands.

Altogether, the Russians obtained the services of several hundred Germans—but these were production engineers and technicians, not top scientists and designers. Their practical experience was very valuable, and saved the Soviet Union a good many months of time in the early stages of its long-range missile program; but the Americans, by skimming off the cream of the design and planning staff, had made an incomparably better bargain. The very few fairly senior men whom the Russians did collect were set to work designing an improved V-2, and when they were drained dry they were sent back to Germany; by 1954 almost all of them had returned to the West without ever having taken part in the real Russian space program. As Von Braun has said: "There is every evidence to believe that their contribution to the Russian space program was almost negligible. They were called upon to write reports about what had happened in the past; but they were squeezed out like lemons, so to speak. In the end, they went home without even being informed about what went on in the classified Russian projects."

The most important of these projects was the development of an intercontinental ballistic missile more than twice the size of the American Atlas. The Russians were forced to develop such large vehicles because their early nuclear weapons were too heavy to be carried by smaller rockets. They did not wait, as did the U.S., until lighter warheads were available. A dictatorship has certain short-term advantages; it is not accountable to the taxpayer.

That huge Soviet booster

By the time the huge Russian ICBM was perfected, improvements in thermonuclear weapons had made it unnecessarily large for military purposes. But it was ideally suited for launching the heavy payloads required for putting men into space. And it had been thoroughly tested; as in any rocket program, there must have been failures, but they were hidden from the world. By the fall of 1957, the U.S.S.R. was in possession of a thoroughly reliable launching vehicle, most probably burning the tried-and-trusted kerosene-liquid-oxygen combination.

That it also had a satellite program should have been a surprise to no one after the summer of 1955; there were numerous references to it in the press and on the radio, and at a Barcelona conference on September 11, 1956, the chairman of the U.S.S.R.'s IGY Committee stated specifically that his country proposed to "launch a satellite by means of which measurement of atmospheric pressure and temperature, as well as observations of cosmic rays, micrometeorites, the geomagnetic field and solar radiation will be conducted. The preparations for launching the satellite are presently being made."

In June of 1957, the Russian magazine *Radio* (the equivalent of the American radio amateurs' *QST*) gave comprehensive instructions for receiving signals from the forthcoming satellites. The frequencies were given (20 and 40 megacycles), as well as characteristics of the orbit and a very clear account of the reception to be expected from a spinning, rapidly moving object in space. This information was not restricted to the U.S.S.R.; all of it was officially passed on to the IGY headquarters and to radio amateurs throughout the world.

The following month, *Radio* ran a notice in its columns. It asked all those who received the satellite transmissions to submit their data to this address: MOSKVA—SPUTNIK

The Man behind "Every . . . Rocket That Flies"

The pictures that make up most of this essay are period photographs. They come from an America and an age that seem terribly remote from a world preparing for interplanetary exploration. At first glance the equipment in most of the pictures may look like the work of a basement tinkerer. In fact the machines are the first working liquid-fuel rockets, and the man who created them was Robert Hutchings Goddard. He was an authentic pioneer. Like Konstantin Tsiolkovsky in Russia and Hermann Oberth in Germany, Goddard worked out calculations on rocketry and space flight, but then he went on to the practical business of designing machinery and equipment, working on fuels, building rockets and actually flying them. Born in Worcester, Massachusetts, in 1882, Goddard was a lone worker who survived recurring illness throughout his youth and endured a derisive press when he proposed plans for space flight. It was years after his death in 1945 that it became apparent that his rockets had not merely survived a changing technology, but had indeed helped create it. As rocket expert Jerome Hunsaker has said, "Every liquid-fuel rocket that flies is a Goddard rocket."

PRELUDE ON AUNT EFFIE'S FARM
On March 16, 1926, Robert Goddard prepared to launch his latest device. After this formal photograph was taken, the rocket was ignited with a blowtorch while Goddard huddled behind a wooden lean-to. The first liquid-fuel rocket took to the air. Flight time: two and one half seconds. Maximum altitude: 41 feet. Distance: 184 feet. Landing site: Aunt Effie's cabbage patch.

limit of balloon; 20 mi

limit of atmos

200

700 miles

- 6 m

1 lb

EARTH

50 lls (H)

Aiming for the Moon in the 1920s

Robert Goddard read H. G. Wells's science-fiction novel of space, *The War of the Worlds*, as a child who was often absent from school because of illness. He was also studious and earnest enough to read the more demanding, less entertaining monthly, *Scientific American*. He first began to think seriously of rocketry and space travel when he was 17. On his own, while majoring in physics at Clark University in Worcester, he began studying possible rocket fuels. After considering various solids, he con-cluded that a combination of liquid hydrogen and liquid oxygen would be the best. Neither was then commercially available. In 1911, at 28, he took his doctorate in physics. A year later he became a teacher at Clark. Though it was not part of the curriculum, Goddard lectured on ways of reaching the moon as well as on more conventional physics subjects.

In 1916, to get funds for further research, Goddard asked the Smithsonian Institution for a grant to build test rockets. He was given $5,000.

ESTHER GODDARD AT 17

A year after her high school graduation, when this photograph was taken, Esther Christine Kisk took a job as secretary at Clark University. Professor Goddard was attracted to the tall, blue-eyed blonde, 19 years his junior. In 1924, after a six-year courtship, they were married.

MOON-FLIGHT FIGURES

With the help of a blackboard diagram, Goddard outlines for his students the problems of reaching the moon by rocket. His calculations —like Oberth's and those of other theorists— showed that a rocket would have to travel seven miles a second to escape the earth's gravity.

THE FIRST RECOILLESS RIFLE

During World War I the Army's Signal Corps commissioned Goddard to design a light, high-power weapon. He developed a small, solid-fuel rocket and launching tube, which he is shown testing here. It was the prototype of the famous antitank bazooka of World War II.

PUMPS THAT FAILED

This 1925 rocket was the first to use fuel pumps *(near base of rocket)*. They had to be small, lightweight, capable of high speeds and of withstanding the low temperature of liquid oxygen. Goddard's pumps were too inefficient. Equipped with these pumps, this small rocket never flew.

"A BIG SITTER"

In 1927 Goddard built a rocket with a combustion chamber 20 times larger than those in his previous rockets. Unlike some of its smaller predecessors, the monster could not lift its own weight. Mrs. Goddard commented sadly, "Instead of a little flier, he had built a big sitter."

Flops
and Successes

In 1920, the Smithsonian Institution made public the monograph which had won Goddard his first research grant. The newspapers pounced on his suggestion for a rocket flight to the moon, and he became known as the "Moon-Rocket Man." A *New York Times* editorial column accused Goddard of lacking "the knowledge daily ladled out in high schools." Movie starlet Mary Pickford asked to send a message in the first rocket to make the trip.

The Smithsonian continued giving him funds throughout the '20s, but its head once expressed disappointment with the results. On receipt of a progress report in which Goddard spoke of space travel, he replied, "Interplanetary space would look much nearer to me after I had seen one of your rockets go up five or six miles in our own atmosphere."

Added to the derision of the press were more serious complaints about the noise of Goddard's tests. One particularly loud flight in 1929 brought ambulances, the police and reporters to Aunt Effie's farm, where he carried out his testing. One newspaper crowed: "Moon Rocket Misses Target by 238,799½ Miles." Thereafter forbidden to test rockets on state land, Goddard moved his operation to Hell Pond, a desolate puddle in the federal artillery range at Camp Devens.

ROCKET WITH HOOP SKIRT
The launching tower for this 1928 rocket was a modified windmill frame which Goddard bought secondhand from a farmer. The hoop, which was designed to add stability to the rocket's flight, kept getting stuck in the tower, but the rocket finally flew, attaining an altitude of 90 feet.

After Hell Pond, Eden Valley

In 1929 an important man, impressed by Goddard's work and excited about the future of rocketry, stepped forward to help him. He was Colonel Charles Lindbergh, America's aviator hero and a good friend of philanthropist Daniel Guggenheim. Soon Goddard received a two-year grant of $50,000. With adequate funds at last, he headed west to Roswell, New Mexico, where the climate and the landscape were perfect for his work. Near Roswell, he set up headquarters at a place called Eden Valley.

Through his years of experimentation Goddard had maintained a correspondence with rocket experts throughout the world. Now he became increasingly troubled by reports of German rocket building. He feared that Germany, unlike the United States, would be quick to recognize the military potential of rockets.

Goddard finally built a device to stabilize the flight of his rockets—a problem which had long plagued him —using a gyroscope, and during the decade at Roswell carried out a static or flight test every three weeks.

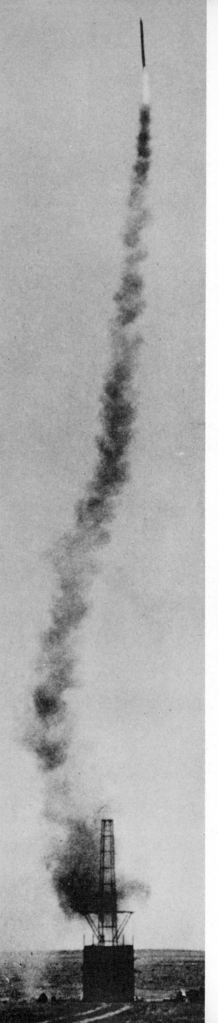

COUNTDOWN IN 1940
His finger on the button, Professor Goddard takes a last look at a new rocket through a telescope. His control board had only three buttons. One ignited the engine, a second operated the rocket's release mechanism. The third cut off the fuel supply in case of emergency.

A CROOKED TRAIL TO SUCCESS
Pointing almost straight up, the smoke trail from this 1937 rocket leaves visible proof of the success of Goddard's gyroscopic stabilizer. Early rockets tipped over too soon and crashed. The new stabilizer, which was connected to two pairs of movable fins, countered this tendency.

"THE HEARSE"
This ancient Model T Ford—Goddard's crew called it "the Hearse"—towed rockets the 10 miles from shop to launching tower. By 1938, when it was replaced by a newer model, it had towed dozens of rockets, and carted many a crash victim back to the shop for repairs.

Goddard and His Rocketeers

AFTER A CRASH LANDING
At the point of impact, Goddard *(third from left)* and part of his crew flank a smashed rocket. With him are welder Charles Mansur, machinist Nils Ljungquist and brother-in-law Albert Kisk.

The proving ground at Eden Valley was manned by a staff which never numbered more than seven: five machinists, including a brother-in-law, Goddard himself, and Mrs. Goddard, official photographer and extinguisher of fires caused by rocket exhausts.

The rockets were almost completely custom-made. Goddard ordered materials from large hardware mail-order houses and his crew prowled through hardware stores, sporting-goods displays and auto-parts outlets. When they found something that might do a particular job—a child's wristwatch, a length of piano wire,

an automobile spark plug—they proceeded to use it to perform a function undreamed of by its manufacturers.

A good deal of time had to be spent in the shop salvaging rockets that were successful—that is, they flew. A rocket that would not take off was a disappointment—but the rocket was usually left intact. A successful flight meant jubilation—and often, carrying home a hunk of junk, all that remained after a crash landing. The smashed rockets could seldom be rebuilt, so Goddard designed and built a rocket recovery system with parachutes to ensure softer landings.

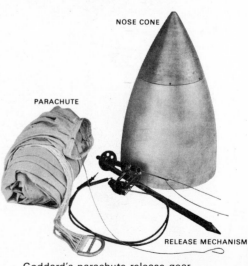

NOSE CONE

PARACHUTE

RELEASE MECHANISM

Goddard's parachute release gear.

AFTER A PERFECT LANDING

From 3,250 feet, this rocket dropped slowly to the floor of Eden Valley, suffering only minor damage. When the rocket began to tip back toward earth, the nose cone was automatically ejected. The small pilot parachute Goddard is inspecting billowed out. It in turn pulled open the main parachute, 10 feet in diameter, which set the 90-pound rocket gently on the ground.

Three Years Ahead of the V-2

By 1939, the year World War II began, thousands of Germans were laboring on the project which would produce the V-2 rocket, first test-flown in 1942. Three years before, Goddard and his small crew in Roswell were building and flying sophisticated rockets like the one shown on these pages.

After America entered World War II, Goddard moved to Annapolis to work for the Government. The Navy asked him to design a rocket-assisted take-off unit for conventional aircraft.

In March, 1945 Goddard saw a captured V-2. Except for size, it was almost identical to his own. (The Germans, incidentally, were amazed at the American Government's lack of interest in Goddard's work.) A few months later, in August, Robert Goddard died. When Wernher Von Braun examined his patents in 1950 he declared, "Goddard was ahead of us all."

In all, Goddard received no fewer than 214 patents covering virtually every aspect of liquid-fuel rockets. In 1960 the United States Government acknowledged his contribution with an award of one million dollars to his estate for the use of his patents. Half the amount was given to the Daniel and Florence Guggenheim Foundation in gratitude for Daniel Guggenheim's initial support of Goddard's dream.

GODDARD'S LAST ROCKET
Goddard (left) and his crew inspect one of his last rockets. Built in 1940, it is in every respect a modern rocket. At the left is the motor (exhaust nozzle and combustion chamber), at the far right are the tanks for the gasoline and liquid oxygen. In the center of the 22-foot vehicle, obscured by the tubes and wires, are the custom-made turbine-operated fuel pumps.

IN THE LAUNCH TOWER
Still to be fitted with nose cone and outer sheathing, the rocket is now being readied for launching by the crew. As always, Goddard (right, opposite) was on hand. At 57 he still clambered up and down the struts of the launch tower, personally inspecting every component.

4

The Satellite Race

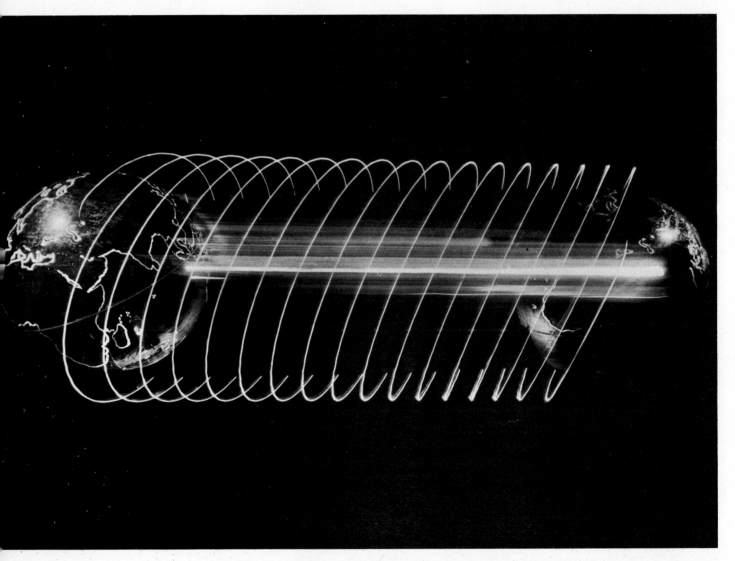

PROFILE OF AN ORBITAL FLIGHT
The spiral path of Russia's second cosmonaut, Gherman Titov, is shown in this photodiagram of his 17-orbit flight in August 1961. During Titov's 25 hours aloft, he traveled 435,000 miles around the earth while being carried an added 1.7 million miles *(left to right)* as the earth moved in its solar orbit. Since Titov's one-day stay, men have remained in space weeks at a time.

*"The great bird will take its first flight on the back of the great
bird, filling the world with stupor and all writings with renown,
and bringing glory to the nest where it was born."*

— LEONARDO DA VINCI, 1505

THE BIRTH CRY OF THE SPACE AGE was probably heard by more men
than any sound in history up to that time. In the days following the
launching of Sputnik on October 4, 1957, millions of people listened
with wonder, pride or fear to the piping electronic voice that circled the
world every 96 minutes. Overnight, the balance of global power had
shifted; the United States had suffered a propaganda setback from which
it was not to recover for years.

Sputnik I had been in orbit just a month when the much larger Sputnik II was launched. The 184-pound payload of the first satellite—almost
10 times that of the projected Vanguard vehicle—had been impressive
enough; the half ton of Sputnik II seemed almost incredible. Moreover,
by carrying the first living creature into orbit—the dog Laika—Sputnik
II gave clear notice of Soviet interest in space biology and, ultimately,
in the launching of a manned spacecraft.

Because of the secrecy with which the Russians had surrounded their
launching vehicles, it was difficult to obtain objective proof of the claims
that they did make. Though no one doubted the existence of satellites
which could be seen with the naked eye, there were some in the West
who refused to believe Russian announcements of their size. All doubts
were removed in mid-December, 1957, when Sputnik II passed over Melbourne Beach, Florida, and was photographed by one of the giant tracking telescopes that monitor the launchings of American rockets.

Though any ordinary camera, loaded with fast film and set for a time
exposure, will record the bright streak produced by a large satellite as it
passes across the stars, very few instruments in the world can produce
an actual image of an object several hundred miles out in space, traveling at 18,000 miles an hour. Normal astronomical telescopes, designed
to follow the slowly moving stars, are useless for the purpose. But the
Melbourne instrument, which had an optical system two feet wide, was
mounted like an antiaircraft gun to follow a target across the sky at satellite speeds. Over a three-day period, tracking Sputnik II on successive
passes, it obtained a whole series of clear pictures.

After the photo interpreters had measured the dumbbell-shaped images on their negatives, they passed on surprising news. Sputnik II,
consisting of the satellite with the final stage of the rocket still attached, was some 80 feet long; the total weight in orbit was estimated
to be as much as six tons.

Just two weeks before this symbol of space superiority passed over the blackened launching pad at Cape Canaveral (later renamed Cape Kennedy), the first attempt to put Vanguard into orbit had been made there. The much-publicized effort had ended in a shattering anticlimax. Kurt Stehling, Vanguard's propulsion engineer, wrote later that as the countdown passed zero, "it seemed as if all the gates of Hell had opened up. Brilliant stiletto flames shot out from the side of the rocket near the engine. The vehicle agonizingly hesitated a moment, quivered again and in front of our unbelieving, shocked eyes, began to topple. It also sank like a great flaming sword into its scabbard down into the blast tube. It toppled slowly, breaking apart, hitting part of the test stand and ground with a tremendous roar that could be felt and heard even behind the 2-foot concrete walls of the blockhouse."

History had been unkind to the members of the Vanguard team. Their project, which originally had been conceived as a purely scientific undertaking, had been swept suddenly into the arena of world politics. The failure of that first orbital attempt on December 6, 1957, was an incident that might have occurred at any time in a development program. As the space age grew older, people would come to understand better the limited chances of bringing off any given shot. It was totally unreasonable to expect immediate success with Vanguard, the very first attempt to launch the complete three-stage version of the most advanced American rocket then in existence.

The oldest satellite

In actual fact the Vanguard program, regarded as a scientific project and not as an entry in an international prestige contest, was highly successful. The three-pound test sphere launched on March 17, 1958, will for centuries have the distinction of being the oldest satellite in orbit, its two heavier Soviet predecessors having long since fallen back to earth. Vanguard II, launched February 17, 1959, reached its design objectives by orbiting a 22-pound payload; Vanguard III far exceeded its objectives by launching a 100-pound payload. Perhaps even more important, the experience gained and the hardware developed during the project were of inestimable value to the entire United States space program for years to come.

After the 1957 failure, however, Vanguard was largely overshadowed by the Army's Explorer satellites. Five days after the launch of Sputnik II, Dr. von Braun and his Huntsville team were given the instructions for which they had been waiting, not exactly patiently, for more than two years. They were told to put a satellite into orbit at the earliest possible moment, and they promised to do so within 90 days.

This promise, amply fulfilled (it took them 84 days), was made possible only by the Huntsville group's previous policy of constructive insubordination. In September 1955 when the Orbiter proposal had been scrapped in favor of Vanguard, the Army had been told to forget about satellites. It did nothing of the sort. Through clever spacemanship, Von Braun had managed to keep the door open by developing a number of multistage Redstone rockets as very-high-speed test vehicles for nose-cone re-entry experiments. It was one of these that attained a velocity only 5,000 mph short of orbital speed in September 1956. Another was carefully salted away in a hangar in case it was needed for a "special project"; Von Braun was fond of showing it to sympathetic visitors with the remark, "This will launch the world's first satellite." In fact, that carefully husbanded missile launched the world's third satellite, but America's first.

Achievements of a busy year

Once started, the Americans outstripped the Russians—in number, if not in the size, of their satellites. It is curious fact that after launching two satellites in quick succession at the end of 1957, the U.S.S.R. put only one, the 3,000-pound Sputnik III, into orbit during the whole of 1958. On the other hand, the United States during its first year in space launched five satellites and three lunar probes. The latter were only partially successful, but they gave scientists their first direct information about regions 70,000 miles above the earth, and they mapped out the limits of the Van Allen belts, previously unsuspected areas of radiation around the earth that had been discovered by Explorer I.

From the American point of view, however, one of the most important events of 1958 was purely organizational. This was the setting up of the National Aeronautics and Space Administration under Dr. T. Keith Glennan. NASA took over the facilities and staff of a predecessor agency, the National Advisory Committee for Aeronautics. When NACA was established in 1915 "to supervise and direct the scientific study of the problems of flight, with a view to their practical solution," Congress voted it a budget of $5,000 a year—"or so much thereof as may be necessary." One cannot help wondering what the cautious legislators of 1915 would have thought had they known that their creation would someday have an offspring that would commence life with a budget roughly 100,000 times larger. (NACA in its first year spent a grand total of $3,938.94.)

NASA, under the technical direction of deputy administrator Dr. Hugh Dryden, wasted no time in making two critical decisions. The first was to organize a man-in-space program. The program was given the name Project Mercury, and the first seven American astronauts were selected from the armed forces. The second was to request top priority for the development of a rocket engine with a thrust of 1.5 million

THE OTHER SIDE OF THE MOON
The moon's far side *(shaded area)* has puzzled man for centuries—until Lunik III photographed it from 43,500 miles in 1959. The pictures, including the one above, were studied closely for data about the newly discovered mountains and "seas" which the Russians named for men such as Aleksandr Popov, who they claim invented radio.

pounds. There was as yet no operational mission for such an engine, but it would require years of development and no one doubted that by the time it was ready it would be needed. (As things turned out, the first vehicle to use this giant engine, the Saturn V, required *five* of them.)

In the first few months of 1958, the tempo of the space age picked up sharply. Over the next five years, some 148 new satellites and probes were sent aloft. They proved their scientific value from the beginning. The first Sputnik had indicated that the density of the atmosphere at which it orbited was five to 10 times greater than anyone had guessed, that temperatures were higher and that the layers of atmosphere surrounding the earth were able to channel the satellite's radio waves to the opposite side of the earth in a "mirror effect." The first American satellite, Explorer I, by first detecting the great radiation zones now known as the Van Allen belts, made the most important scientific discovery of the International Geophysical Year. Even the three-pound, grapefruit-sized Vanguard I did its share for science by giving mankind the first clue that the world it lived on was pear-shaped *(pages 116 and 117)*.

Moon shot, moon dream

Less than a year after the ushering in of the space age, the United States turned its efforts toward the moon. Three successive probes, Pioneers I, II and III, launched a month apart in late 1958, experienced failures in propulsion. The Soviets made the next try for the moon, in 1959, and had a failure of their own. Initially the Soviet probe was called Lunik for "moon shot," but the Russians later renamed it Mechta, or "dream." It went on to become the first spacecraft to go into an orbit around the sun. Two months later the United States fired off Pioneer IV; it suffered almost precisely the same fate as Lunik-Mechta, missing the moon by some 37,300 miles and plunging into solar orbit.

Superior Soviet rocketry finally paid off in this lunar shooting match. The Russians scored a direct hit near the center of the moon with a Lunik on September 12, 1959. A few weeks later Lunik III provided the most exciting souvenirs to come from space up to that time by transmitting back to earth some crude aerial photographs of the moon's back side, hitherto unseen by man.

Ironically, the United States was more successful in attempts to garner close-hand information about the planet Venus, 24 million miles away at its closest approach to earth. The Soviets made the first try on February 12, 1961, firing a 1,419-pound Venus probe from the seven-ton Sputnik VIII, circling in orbit about the earth. But the Russians' Venus ship had proceeded only about a week on its three-month trip when its radio went dead.

Venus only occasionally came near enough to the earth for the spacecraft of the early 1960s to reach it, and the next opportunity did not arise until more than a year later. The United States was ready with two Mariner spacecraft and the Atlas rockets to fire them. The first, fired on July 22, 1962, veered off course and had to be destroyed; something had gone wrong with the guidance equations that were stored in the Atlas' computer brain. The Americans had 50 more days before the planet got too far away. On August 26, Mariner II left the launch pad, and NASA scientists proceeded to demonstrate that although the U.S.S.R. might still be ahead in rockets, the U.S. could perform some wonderful tricks with them.

At first Mariner II seemed headed for trouble. It developed a strange roll, and ground controllers thought for a time that it would have to be destroyed in flight. Then at the last moment it settled down. The spacecraft separated from its first-stage rocket and headed out into the solar system. After it had been on its way about a week, scientists checking its course discovered that it was going to miss Venus by some 233,000 miles. They thereupon sent a course correction to Mariner II by radio—over a distance of nearly 1.5 million miles, the longest radio transmission ever attempted successfully—and altered the orbit of the craft. After 109 days, Mariner II passed triumphantly within 21,600 miles of Venus.

On its long voyage it had reported back a number of fascinating facts about outer space; now it reported many new discoveries about Venus: that its surface temperature, as prophesied, appeared to be extremely high; that its cloud cover appeared to be about 15 miles thick and 45 miles above the planet's surface; that it had no magnetic field or Van Allen belt. As the probe passed Venus, scientists on earth calculated the planet's mass accurately for the first time by measuring the course deviation caused by Venusian gravity.

Man joins a menagerie

The Venus probe was an exciting accomplishment, but of all the satellite contests between Soviets and Americans the one that inevitably captured the greatest attention was the race to get men into space *(pages 85-97)*. Following in the orbital path of the dog Laika, whole menageries of live creatures—rats, mice, flies, monkeys, chimpanzees—were sent aloft by the Russians and the Americans in the months following Sputnik II. Some of the dangers of space travel were indicated when two of the Russians' test satellites suffered catastrophes: one burned up on re-entry, and the other, on a signal to return to earth, went instead into a higher orbit. Nevertheless, it was the Russians who in April 1961 first succeeded in sending up a man, Yuri Gagarin. He landed after a single orbit. The United States was a poor second; on May 5, 1961, the first American space traveler, Navy Commander Alan B. Shepard Jr., made a

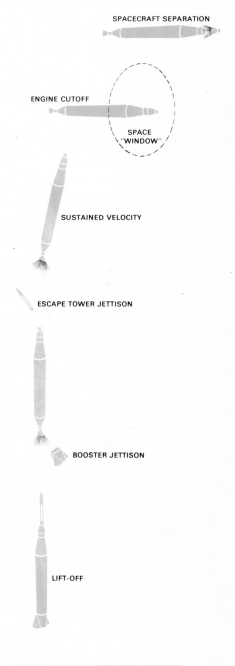

SPACECRAFT SEPARATION

ENGINE CUTOFF

SPACE "WINDOW"

SUSTAINED VELOCITY

ESCAPE TOWER JETTISON

BOOSTER JETTISON

LIFT-OFF

LAUNCHING A SPACE TRAVELER
Astronauts orbited in the Mercury project were launched in a 3,000-pound capsule atop a 67-foot Atlas rocket. By two minutes and 33 seconds after launch, booster and escape tower (which in a misfire was to blast the capsule out of danger) were jettisoned. Then the second stage, aimed at a precise area in space—rocket men call it the "window" through which the vehicle must pass—sent the capsule into orbit at about 17,500 mph.

79

ballistic flight rather than an orbital one. The Americans did not put a man into orbit until February 1962, when Marine Colonel John Glenn went up for three circuits—and by then a Russian had orbited 17 times. Still, even though the U.S.S.R. had won this race as it had others, the United States achieved a success of its own by giving fascinated viewers the world over a grandstand seat by television as it completed its series of successful shots in the Mercury Program.

The Russians, with their head start in rocket size, had been consistently able to carry off most of the dramatic honors in these first years of the space age. But the United States, with its better instrumentation, seemed to be putting its satellites to more effective use, employing them for weather observation, communications, navigation, biological studies and for various military purposes, some of them secret.

Viewing the weather

The initial primitive attempts at weather observation began in 1959 with Vanguard II, which contained light-sensitive cells that were supposed to provide information about the earth's cloud cover. Unfortunately, the tumbling of the satellite made the data unreadable. Explorer VI in the same year was more successful, but it was the Tiros I weather satellite of April 1960 that really elated weathermen. It transmitted to earth 22,952 photographs of cloud patterns, presaging a whole series of satellites that were to prove useful in day-to-day weather forecasting.

Twelve days after Tiros, the U.S. launched another valuable satellite, Transit I, a navigation beacon for ships.

The first NASA communications satellite was Echo I, launched August 12, 1960. After attaining orbital altitude, it unfolded into a 100-foot silvery balloon. The balloon caught the rays of the sun and was clearly visible from earth; its stately passage across the nighttime sky enchanted viewers from the ground for years afterward. More important, its reflective surface proved the feasibility of bouncing radio signals around the world. Differing from this "passive" type of communications satellite was the Army's Courier I, which contained tape recorders that could store messages sent to it, then carry them around the world and rebroadcast them to a receiving station. It was launched in the October following the orbiting of Echo. Far more sophisticated communications satellites were soon in orbit, making it possible among other things for viewers to see live television programs simultaneously in distant parts of the world.

On February 28, 1959, the U.S. Air Force fired a satellite called Discoverer I into an orbit over the poles. Since the earth rotated under its stationary orbit, Discoverer I could view the entire earth's surface, unlike other satellites which could view only a belt around the equator.

MERCURY CONTROL PANEL

The "dashboard" of a Mercury capsule is diagramed at right as it appeared to an astronaut. The flight-control systems have attitude and velocity indicators, ways of switching to automatic or manual control, and meters that tell time from launch and time to retro-rocket firing. The communications systems handle both voice and automatic radio signals. In the "miscellaneous" section is a window through which photographs can be taken.

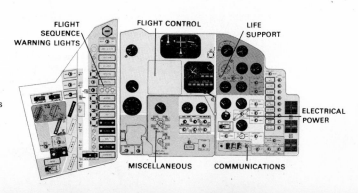

FLIGHT SEQUENCE WARNING LIGHTS

FLIGHT CONTROL

LIFE SUPPORT

ELECTRICAL POWER

MISCELLANEOUS

COMMUNICATIONS

Thus it paved the way for later American and Russian reconnaissance satellites, which took advantage of similar orbits. In April 1959 a Discoverer actually returned to earth a capsule that may have been carrying exposed camera film, but the capsule was lost at sea. A long series of similar failures plagued the Discoverer program (one capsule may even have been recovered by the Russians). It was not until August 10, 1960, on the 13th try, that a payload ejected from orbit was actually recovered. Not long afterward the Soviets let it be known that they too were employing camera-bearing satellite spies. Later Samos and Midas reconnaissance satellites also were launched by the United States to detect the unannounced firing of missiles by the use of television cameras and heat-sensing infrared equipment.

By the fifth year of the space age, the total number of satellites and space probes had grown so large that their complete listing would have run to several pages of print. Besides the Sputniks, the Russians had put aloft a Cosmos series of scientific satellites that now numbered 12. The U.S. Explorers had reached 16, and no less than 38 Discoverer satellites had been launched. In addition, throughout 1962 the U.S. Air Force had launched classified satellites at the rate of about three a month. The total box score for the year was at least United States 61, U.S.S.R. 17, and the giant computers of the tracking centers were kept busy maintaining the tally of the several hundred individual objects in orbit. There were innumerable wires, nose cones, spent rockets and other pieces of hardware circling the earth. One satellite, Transit 4A, launched on June 29, 1961, had added enormously to the confusion by exploding into more than 150 separate fragments, each traveling in its own independent orbit.

The lifetime of a satellite

Some of the satellites of the first half decade were short-lived, burning up like meteors when they re-entered the atmosphere after a few revolutions around the earth, but others remained at such great altitudes that it was clear they would be aloft for centuries. The lifetime of a satellite is determined by its closest approach to earth (its perigee height). If it comes within 80 to 100 miles, air drag will bring it down in a few days, and final disintegration will occur at an altitude of about 50 miles.

One of the most spectacular astronautical events ever observed was the death of Sputnik II. By pure coincidence, the orbit of the closest possible satellite—one just grazing the atmosphere, to put it rather unscientifically—is very nearly 90 minutes. Because this is an exact fraction of a day, every dying satellite will make its final appearance at the same time and in the same part of the sky for several successive days

MERCURY'S "LIFE SUPPORT"

Much of a spaceman's comfort as well as life itself hinges on the operation of the vital life support system in his capsule (simplified in the diagram at right). The system regulates air pressure at all times. It inhales stale air from the suit and cabin, oxygenates and purifies it, and sends it to the air-conditioning unit. There excess water vapor is shot overboard and the air is brought to the proper temperature before being returned to the astronaut.

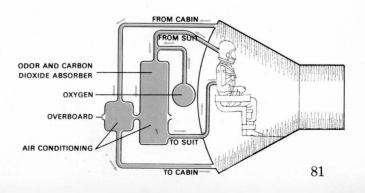

immediately before its descent. The turning globe will have brought it back to an almost identical spot in the heavens.

Thus on the last three nights of its existence, Sputnik II sailed like a brilliant star across England soon after dusk, witnessed by millions of awed watchers. In the early morning hours of April 14, 1958, it re-entered the denser layers of the atmosphere over the Caribbean; as seen from Barbados, it was several times brighter than Venus—a dazzling comet spitting off blazing globules of light which trailed across a quarter of the sky. Almost half the population of the island was privileged to watch the first man-made meteor shower.

There are other satellites, however, whose descent will be so far in the future that there may be no humans to witness it. Some of the Midas missile detectors, 2,000 miles high, may still be orbiting in the year 100,000 A.D. And such deep-space probes as Mariner II and Mars I, which have escaped from earth completely, will be permanent members of the solar system. Even if our civilization destroys itself utterly in some thermonuclear holocaust, it will leave some relics drifting in eternal orbits round the sun—perhaps for the bafflement of alien explorers ages hence.

Terrors of the imagination

Because the dangers of the unknown always appear more threatening than those of the known, space had seemed filled with many terrors before men launched themselves forth into it. Just as the cartographers of old used to write such phrases as "Here Be Dragons" in the wide blanks of their maps, so pre-Sputnik space was held to be filled with perils. Not all of them were imaginary. No one doubted that once men ventured beyond the screen of the atmosphere they would have to be provided with air and protected against the surrounding vacuum. But no one doubted, either, that this could be done by straightforward extensions of existing technology. Since the stratosphere flights of the 1930s, manned balloons and aircraft had been operating in regions which were, physiologically, almost as hostile as space. The human lung can hardly notice the difference between one twentieth of an atmosphere (encountered in the famous 1935 flight of the U.S. Army-National Geographic Society balloon, Explorer II) and no atmosphere at all.

Yet that last small percentage of air, thinning away across a hundred miles of altitude, is of vital importance to life on earth. It shields us almost completely from dangerous radiation, and from the incessant downpour of meteors which bombard our planet at the rate of many millions every day. There were those who believed before 1957 that neither men nor vehicles could survive for long outside the protective blanket of the atmosphere.

But even the first satellites showed that the danger from meteorites had been grossly overestimated by the pessimists. One day a spacecraft will be badly damaged by a meteorite, but it has not happened yet. And the danger from the known cosmic radiations had also been greatly exaggerated; with the possible exception of the solar flares, the hazard they presented was almost negligible. That was why the discovery of the great radiation belts around the earth was a considerable shock. Here was a hitherto unknown but very real peril, which made certain regions of space uninhabitable without a prohibitive weight of shielding. However, it was soon realized that the Van Allen belts represented an obstacle to be bypassed, not a complete roadblock. By choosing suitable orbits it is possible to avoid the most intense levels of radiation—and to outward-bound spacecraft the belts are no serious menace, for a ship will flash through them swiftly.

Worries of weightlessness

The other great hobgoblin of space flight had been weightlessness, or zero gravity, as it is often called. This last name is technically inaccurate, for an astronaut in an orbiting satellite is just as much under the influence of gravity as when he is standing on the ground. However, because he is no longer resisting it but is letting it act upon him unhindered, the feeling of weight which gravity normally produces is gone. The situation is exactly the same as in a freely falling elevator cage: occupants will float in mid-air. But an elevator can fall for only a few seconds, whereas a spaceship can "fall" forever around the earth, or around the sun.

Because weightlessness had never been experienced by human beings for more than a fraction of a minute, there was fear that it might produce uncontrollable nausea, lack of muscular coordination, runaway beating of the heart and a host of other dangerous changes in the body's functioning. The week-long flight of Laika in Sputnik II was of the utmost importance in setting these fears to rest. Today we know that weightlessness, far from being unpleasant, can be delightful. To be sure, nobody knows what effect long-term weightlessness might have. Some scientists even see a possibility that astronauts' bodies, once adapted to weightlessness, might find it hard to reconvert to earth's gravity after many weeks of flight in space.

In any case, the first few years of the space age demolished many myths, opened up the greatest frontier in history and reoriented men's minds in ways that few of them have yet realized. A proof of this is the fact that on August 6, 1961, a Russian Air Force major flew directly over Washington without asking permission and without causing any protests. Although no formal agreements had been drawn up, it was already understood that the law of the air could not apply to outer space, and that it would be ridiculous even to attempt its extension. (That did not stop the U.S.S.R. from continuing to protest after Titov's flight over Washington that the Midas reconnaissance satellite was violating its territorial sovereignty. The protests ceased after the Russians got their own reconnaissance satellites into orbit.) It is now generally recognized that a country can claim jurisdiction over the "air space" above its own borders; that is all. No one had ever defined the meaning of "air space" (now seen as rather an unfortunate hybrid term), but it clearly could not extend to infinity. Otherwise, as the earth turned on its axis during a single day, every large country would lay claim to most of the universe.

And there were other absurdities as well, when one tried to extend earth-based thinking beyond the atmosphere. Soviet Major Gherman Titov could maintain, with perfect truth, that his orbit was fixed in space; he merely retraced the same circle for 17 revolutions. It was not *his* fault if the city of Washington, racing madly eastward at about 800 miles an hour, moved directly underneath him at one point as the earth spun on its axis.

Out on the new frontier, it would be necessary to start anew and to discard old ways of thought. And that, perhaps, was the greatest hope of the age that had now dawned.

Pioneers in a Strange New World

The period following the launching of Sputnik in October 1957 saw two nations compete in a strange and fruitful endeavor known popularly as "the space race." Within a few years, man's horizons were permanently changed by the soaring missiles, vast testing bases and extensive networks of tracking stations created by America and the Soviet Union. The space programs of the two countries differed notably but inconclusively. At first, the more powerful Russian rockets scored many firsts. Then the Americans made history with the first rendezvous and docking in space. In seesaw competition, both programs moved swiftly to achieve mastery of the multi-orbit flight; and they made a manned moon landing so certain that only the exact date remained in doubt. In this dramatic opening up of the unknown world beyond earth, the imagination of people everywhere was captured by the exploits of a new breed of pioneer, the spacemen.

THUMBS UP FOR SPACE
Safely down, Air Force Major Edward White gives a triumphant thumbs-up as he and Major James McDivitt are greeted on the recovery ship *Wasp* after a 1965 mission in which White became the first American to walk in space. Following the excited welcome, the two men headed for medical tests which showed they had suffered no ill effects from their four days of unearthly adventure.

First into Space, Animal Scouts

On November 3, 1957, the Soviet Union electrified the world by putting into orbit Sputnik II, carrying the world's first orbiting passenger—an 11-pound dog named Kudryavka, or Little Curly, who came to be known throughout the world by the name of her breed, Laika. Although she died in orbit, Laika contributed valuable biomedical information about space. Other dogs followed—among them Strelka (below) and Belka, the first animals safely recovered from orbit. And since the Soviets continue to precede manned spectaculars with animal flights, the first earthling on the moon may well be a dog.

Americans probed the dangers of rocket flight with animals, starting as early as 1948, when a nine-pound rhesus monkey was launched in a V-2 nose cone. Tests continued with other animals until January 1961. On that date the chimpanzee Ham was shot on a 414-mile, 16.5-minute flight in a production model of the Mercury capsule. The next passenger launched in the Project Mercury series was the self-styled "link between Ham and man"—astronaut Alan Shepard.

ON CAMERA: AN ORBITING CANINE
The dog Strelka, companion of Belka aboard Sputnik V in August 1960, appears in profile in this Russian television closeup transmitted from the capsule during the dogs' 18-orbit flight Strelka later had a litter of six puppies, one of which was sent to President John F. Kennedy.

SIMULATING A SPACE FLIGHT
Outfitted for space in a pressurized suit and mask with oxygen hose attached, a dog follows a Soviet scientist into a pressure chamber to conduct a simulated flight. As early as 1949, the Russians began using animals on ballistic shots Before sending them aloft, the Russians put the animals through months of rigorous training to prepare them for flight conditions.

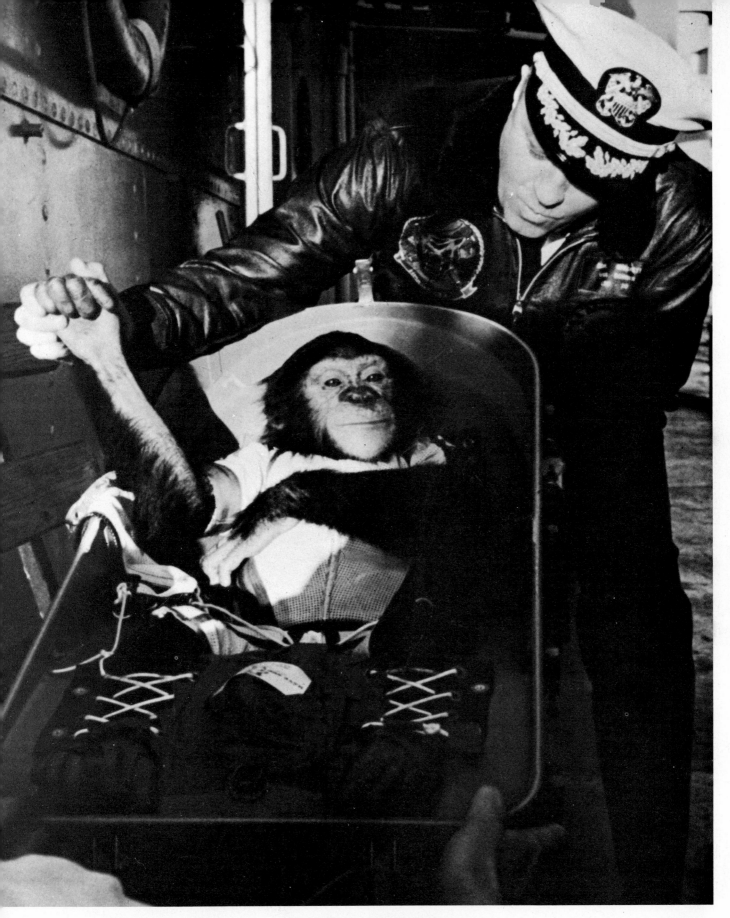

HAPPY END TO A LENGTHY RIDE

The chimpanzee Ham, safe aboard his rescue ship, grapples playfully with a naval officer. Other Project Mercury anthropoids also emerged from their flights unscathed. But several space-going monkeys in earlier American tests did not survive mishaps like Ham's: on launching, his rocket's thrust control jammed open, propelling him some 120 miles farther than planned.

A Bumper Crop of Soviet Heroes

The manned phase of Russian space efforts began in typical Soviet style —unannounced until crowned with smashing success. On April 12, 1961, Yuri Gagarin *(below, left)* became the first human being to arrive in space; his Vostok I capsule whirled one full orbit, then thudded down safely on a Russian collective farm. Four months later, Gherman S. Titov topped this feat with a 17-orbit flight.

The Soviet exploits that followed were even showier. In August 1962, Andrian Nikolayev in Vostok III and Pavel Popovich in Vostok IV went up one day apart, circled the globe simultaneously for 70 hours, and came down within six minutes of each other. Another two-ship launching in June 1963 included the first woman in space, 26-year-old Valentina Tereshkova *(below)*. She made 48 orbits in Vostok VI; Valery Bykovsky, her companion in space, stayed up for 81 orbits. Then in October 1964 the Russians launched the first three-man spacecraft, Voskhod I. The crew, a cosmonaut-pilot, a scientist-spacecraft designer, and a physician, rode into orbit without pressure suits. The second Voskhod flight had a crew of only two *(opposite)*, but one of them made the first walk in space, a signal of more spectaculars to come.

"I WAS IN A BALL OF FIRE"
Major Yuri A. Gagarin stares resolutely through the facepiece of his space helmet in this Russian photograph. During re-entry, as the 27-year-old cosmonaut later recalled graphically, "I saw the lurid glow of flames raging around the ship. I was in a ball of fire plunging downward."

"THIS IS SEAGULL"
Valentina Tereshkova, formerly a mill hand and later the bride of cosmonaut Andrian Nikolayev, is seen training for her flight. As she went into orbit, she radioed, "This is Seagull. I feel fine and cheerful. I see the horizon. A pale blue, blue stripe. It's the earth. How beautiful it is."

"I SAW THE ENDLESS FACE OF EARTH"

The crew of Voskhod II peer out of their opened helmets during their eventful flight. Lieutenant Colonel Alexei Leonov *(right)* sits with his shoulder against a porthole; Colonel Pavel Belyayev holds a control stick with his ungloved hand. Of his space walk, Leonov said, "I saw the endless face of earth, half of the globe. I saw our country from the Black Sea to Sakhalin Island."

In Project Mercury, "All Systems Go"

On May 5, 1961, amid continuing excitement over Gagarin's orbital flight of three weeks before, America's Project Mercury sent a man into space. While millions watched on television, astronaut Alan B. Shepard *(opposite)* was launched on a 15-minute, 302-mile suborbital shot over the Atlantic. It went flawlessly. "All systems go," he kept reporting in the space team's jargon. And the United States had its first space hero. The Project Mercury shots that followed were not all as smooth, but despite troubles ranging from faulty steering and electrical systems to overheating of the capsule, not a man was lost. Virgil Grissom followed Shepard on a suborbital flight in July. Then on February 20, 1962, John Glenn *(right)* blasted aloft to become the world's third orbiting spaceman and America's first. In May, Scott Carpenter followed for three orbits. Walter Schirra, orbiting in October, went for six. The final shot in the series came in May 1963, when Gordon Cooper *(right, below)* orbited for 22 circuits, the longest of the Mercury flights.

The purpose of Project Mercury was to accumulate knowledge about man's capabilities in space for use in the subsequent Gemini and Apollo programs. This mission was accomplished. President John F. Kennedy described Cooper's flight in words that could well have applied to the whole effort when he called it "one of the victories of the human spirit."

GLAD TO BE DOWN SAFE
Sweat-soaked Major Gordon Cooper grins from the open hatch of his capsule, secure on board the USS *Kearsarge* after 34 hours in space. Faulty automatic steering forced Cooper to use manual controls to re-enter, but he hit the target as he had predicted: "right on the old bazoo."

MAKEREADY AT LAUNCH PAD 5
At 5:14 on launch day, Lieutenant Commander Alan Shepard steps from a transport van and strides toward the floodlit Redstone missile on what was then Cape Canaveral Launch Pad 5. He carries a small air-conditioning unit that regulates the temperature inside his pressure suit.

A HISTORIC MISSION COMPLETED
Lieutenant Colonel John Glenn, leaving his rescue ship by helicopter, heads for debriefing. Despite malfunctioning controls and a warning light that indicated his capsule might incinerate on re-entry, he rode it for three orbits before splashing down perfectly into the Atlantic Ocean. Five of the six Mercury pilots managed to land within sight of a waiting recovery ship.

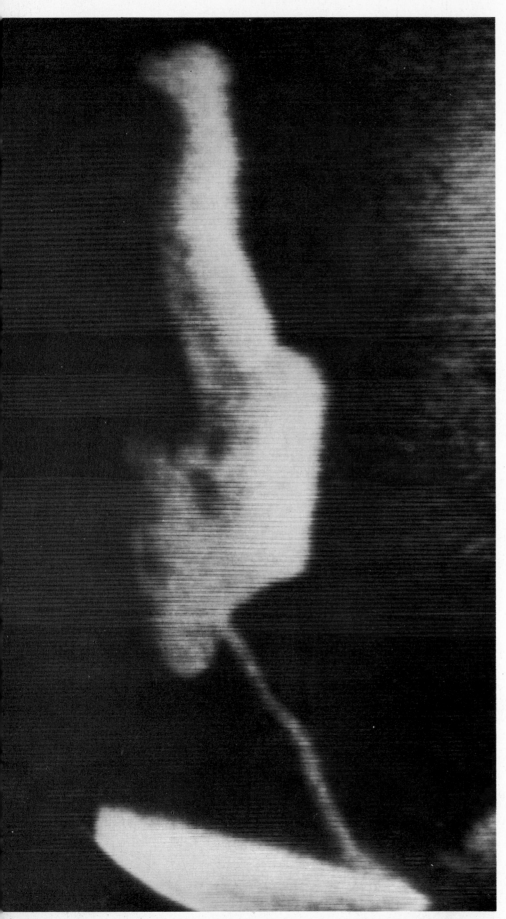

Stepping Out into the Void

During the Soviet Union's eighth manned space flight, in March 1965, Lieutenant Colonel Alexei A. Leonov, 30, pushed himself out of an air lock of his 13,000-pound Voskhod II capsule. While earthbound countrymen watched on television, pilot Pavel Belyayev announced: "Man has stepped out into cosmic space." It was another Russian "first." For 10 minutes Leonov maneuvered alone at the end of a 16-foot, wire-rope tether. "I felt absolutely free," he said, "soaring like a bird."

Just 77 days later, U.S. astronaut Edward White followed Leonov into space. White remained outside his Gemini 4 capsule for 20 minutes, maneuvering part of the time with jets of compressed oxygen. Deadly space hazards surrounded him: sun-heated temperatures outside his pressurized suit ranging as high as 250° F.; cosmic radiation; speeding micrometeorites. (White's suit had 22 different layers for protection against heat, radiation or the penetrating impact of particles of matter.)

The success of both space walks proved that man can work effectively in space, and further assignments were sure to come. Despite the dangers of his adventure, when ordered to return to his ship White said, "It's the saddest moment of my life."

A TELEVISED SPACE "WALK"
Apparently floating helplessly, head downward, Alexei Leonov drifts at the end of his tether as televised to earth from Voskhod II. Actually in space there is no up or down, so one's bodily position is immaterial. "Everything is well," he reported at the time, "and I feel excellent."

120 MILES ABOVE THE PACIFIC
Trailing the 25-foot-long, gold-coated umbilical cord that carries his oxygen, Edward White propels himself away from Gemini 4 with his jet gun to get a clear view of the cloud-strewn water below. At bottom right is the open hatch door through which he stepped out into space.

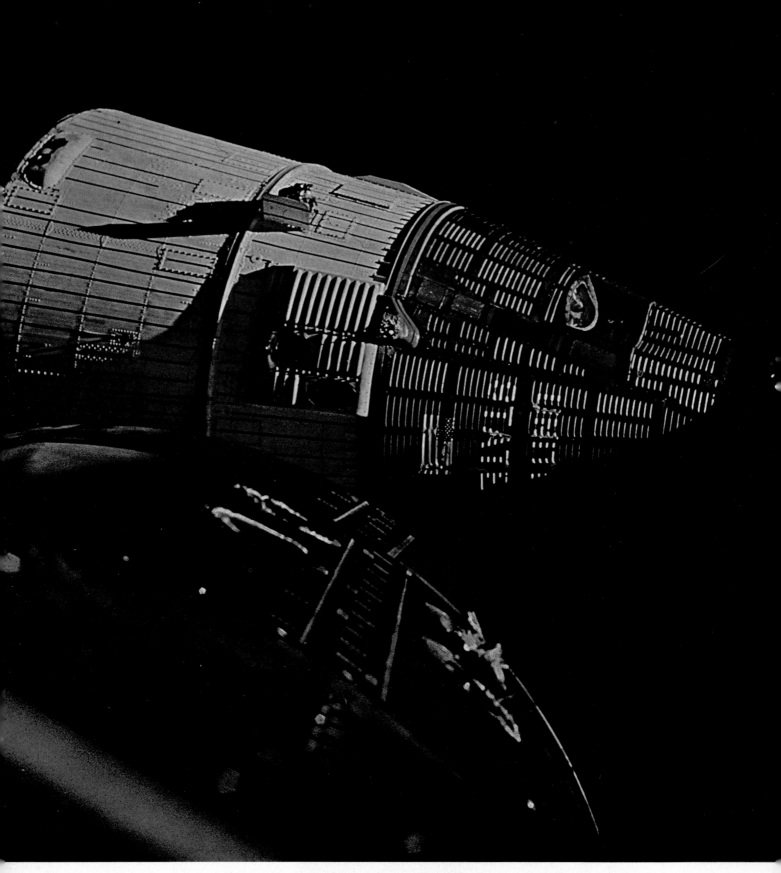

A MEETING OF SPACE VOYAGERS
Like one curious monster examining another, Gemini 6 circles Gemini 7, nearing the end of a historic 14-day flight. Up and down, back and forth Gemini 6 maneuvered with short bursts of its 16 thrusters, coming finally to within one foot of its sister capsule—a feat proving that stranded astronauts could be rescued and that satellite platforms can soon be built in space.

The First
Space Rendezvous

"We are 120 feet apart and sitting." The voice was calm, but every word carried an unmistakable note of triumph. Some engineers had feared that capsule pilots might never be able to adapt well enough to the topsy-turvy world of orbital mechanics to bring two vehicles safely together in space. But the job was done. In December 1965 U.S. Navy Captain Walter Schirra showed that close-range maneuvering of a spacecraft orbiting at 17,500 miles an hour was, as he described it, "a piece of cake."

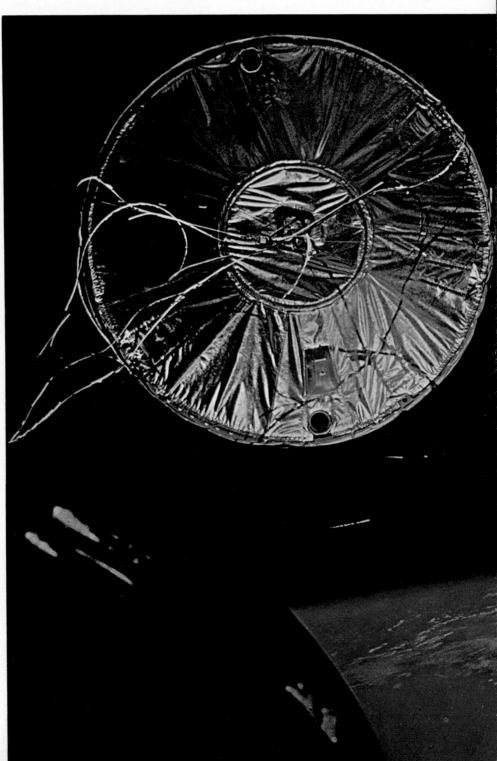

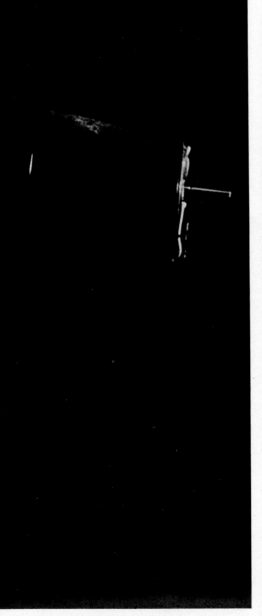

A GOLDEN DISK IN THE SKY
In the eerie void, Gemini 7's plastic thermal blanket, which protects a vital instrument package, gleams in the sun. The spaghettilike tails are tie-down tapes torn loose after the launch.

A Perilous Return to Earth

At the end of a mission in space come a few minutes fraught with their own special hazards: the period of the return to earth. Computers make the necessary trajectory calculations, but these cannot always be followed exactly. In the Gemini 4 flight, the retro-rockets, fired by hand because of a malfunction, started one second too soon—and the capsule landed 56 miles off target. On the way down, atmospheric friction—a major peril for spacecraft—heats the capsule's ceramic shield to 3,000° F. Slowed to 30 feet per second by parachutes, the capsule splashes into the sea, which somewhat cushions the final impact of landing. (Russian spacemen frequently try to land in deep snow for the same effect; on some flights they have ejected themselves from the capsule, landing with their own parachutes for added safety.)

Highly trained frogmen of the Navy Air-Sea Rescue Service go quickly to the aid of downed U.S. astronauts. Wherever needed, they drop to the sea from airplane or helicopter to prevent the capsule's sinking—a misfortune which marred the otherwise perfect Mercury 2 flight. Then the spacemen, taken to the recovery ship, can report: "Mission accomplished."

AFTER THE SPLASHDOWN
Safely buoyed by yellow flotation gear attached by Navy frogmen, Gemini 6 lies awash 14 miles from its recovery ship as astronauts Thomas Stafford and Walter Schirra climb out of their cramped quarters. For the spacemen the trip is all over except for the drudgery of comprehensive physical examinations and debriefing.

5

Tireless
Servants
in the Sky

What use are the Van Allen belts?   I make a living out of them.
                              —Dr. James Van Allen

Dr. Van Allen's facetious remark contains a profound truth. One day, millions will indeed be "making a living" out of space. If this seems fantastic, consider what has already happened with aviation. When the first flimsy airplanes staggered off the ground, few people believed that they would be of much practical importance. Even the Wright brothers at first thought that aircraft would be useful mainly for sport and, perhaps, military reconnaissance. The most enthusiastic pioneers of aviation never dreamed of a world transformed by flight.

But within a single lifetime, the airplane has become the world's primary mode of long-range passenger transportation. Today, thousands fly where once Lindbergh traveled alone, and there is hardly a human being on this planet who has not been affected in some way by the conquest of the air. Will this story be repeated in space? The analogy seems obvious, yet it is false in some respects—the significance of the airplane may be slight compared to that of space travel.

The airplane only gave us swifter access to places in which men were already living. The realm now being opened up by space vehicles is so immeasurably greater than all the lands and seas of earth that any comparison fails utterly. Not only will space vehicles place the planets within our reach, they will also help to revolutionize human life on this planet. Consider, for example, the single field of communications.

Prior to 1956, it was not possible for people on opposite sides of the Atlantic Ocean to speak with one another except by radiotelephone. And if atmospheric conditions were bad, it was sometimes not possible to speak across the Atlantic at all. Then, in 1956, the first transatlantic telephone cable went into operation and provided 36 static-free telephone circuits.

A mere six years later, Telstar I, the first transatlantic-relay communications satellite, was hurled into orbit. By future standards, it will doubtless seem a primitive device. Yet, alone it could handle nearly a thousand simultaneous telephone conversations.

Furthermore, Telstar I (and its successors) was not limited merely to voice communications. It also had the ability to relay television signals across the width of the Atlantic. For technical reasons, television images can be carried only on very short waves, but these, like light, can travel only a straight line-of-sight path. On land, therefore, long-distance television broadcasting requires the use either of expensive coaxial cables or relay chains of tall microwave towers, each within sight of its nearest neighbors.

SATELLITES FOR COMMUNICATION
A control operator checks television reception relayed by a Telstar communications satellite orbiting 600 to 6,700 miles above the earth. The station, at Goonhilly Downs, England, is one of the original three receiving Telstar's 2 1/4-watt telephone and television signals—the beginning of a network intended to blanket the entire globe with instantaneous communication.

To transmit a television signal across the Atlantic would have required either a technically impractical coaxial cable or else a fleet of ships, each with a 100-foot relay tower and each accurately positioned, perhaps 100 of them altogether. Yet Telstar I, measuring only a trifle less than three feet across, accomplished this same purpose. In a very real sense, it provided a microwave tower several thousand miles high, electronically visible simultaneously from Europe and America.

Telstar's achievements, remarkable as they have been, are merely the feeblest first steps along the road opened up by communications satellites—or "comsats," as they are sometimes called. Already we can foresee a time when a global network of advanced satellites will bring all points of the earth into immediate contact—by radio, television, telephone, facsimile and every other form of telecommunication.

Preparing for that day, Congress in 1963 created the Communications Satellite Corporation (the first company chartered by the Government since an 1862 act created the Union Pacific Railroad). Soon 45 Free World nations joined in the planning for a worldwide system. The system's first satellite, Early Bird, was launched April 6, 1965, providing 240 telephone circuits or one television channel between North America and Europe. In addition, the Defense Department orbited its own satellites. And the Russians, who had not joined the corporation, launched a Soviet satellite, foreshadowing, perhaps, their own system.

There is no doubt that the millions of channels opened up by the satellites will eventually make possible that old dream of science fiction, person-to-person contact, anywhere in the world, through equipment no larger than a wristwatch. Such personalized transceivers may very well make it just as easy to telephone Australia from Greenland, or South America from Japan, as it is now to dial a local number. In fact, by the end of this century, *all* terrestrial calls may be "local" ones, billed at a single rate, since distance, no matter how great, will be immaterial.

The price of progress

There is, of course, a reverse side of this appealing picture. Many people will be appalled at the prospect of living in a world where escape from one's fellow men becomes difficult—when we may be called, at any hour of the day or night, by anyone, even on the other side of the earth. Of course, a person could turn off his transceiver—but that might mean missing an important call.

In any case, there seems little doubt that society will accept the minor disadvantages of comsats in exchange for the enormous gains. At the very least, comsats and personalized transceivers will banish forever the exasperation of waiting on a corner for a friend while he mistakenly waits for you on another. Far beyond that, such personal receivers will

TRIBUTES TO AMERICAN FIRSTS

Two satellites have been honored on postage stamps. The U.S. stamp above commemorates Echo I, NASA's first communications satellite, which was orbited on August 12, 1960. A French stamp *(right)* depicts the first commercial satellite, A.T. & T.'s Telstar. Far smaller and more sophisticated than Echo I, it relayed the first television signals to cross the Atlantic, from Andover, Maine, to Pleumeur-Bodou, France, in July 1962.

save thousands of lives every year. Each transceiver will have an SOS button which can be pressed in an emergency to send out a distress signal; countless human tragedies will thus be averted, and certain categories of crime greatly reduced.

The personal transceiver might also make a genuine democracy practical for the first time since the days of Athens. Issues of public interest could be put to the vote of an entire nation, and the result reported by computers in a matter of seconds—one by-product of rockets that some politicians may consider infinitely more terrifying than the ICBM with a nuclear warhead.

Bridge between the continents

Trying to list all the possible ramifications of communications satellites at the present time is a little like having attempted in 1800 to forecast all the conceivable applications of electricity. The most important developments, it is certain, will be overlooked. But here are a few which seem inevitable:

The orbital post office. The very first Telstar could transmit more than the word output of 18,000 typists. One day there will be direct facsimile links between all major towns, so that exact copies of letters can be delivered to almost any region on earth only minutes after the letters are posted.

The orbital newspaper. What the public requires from the press is information, and it need not be printed on paper. Perhaps a generation from now, when a man wishes to read his daily paper he will dial some designated numbers from among the thousands of available television channels and see the paper screened before him. Editorials will be on one channel, sports, book reviews, science, drama, advertising on others. A few giant newspapers (if indeed that name survives) will cover the world, for it will be just as easy to receive the latest *New York Times* in Tristan da Cunha as in Manhattan.

Global conference facilities. Communications satellites will make unnecessary much of the present intercontinental junketing on the part of politicians, administrators and other people who travel regularly on business. Instead, it will be a simple matter to hold a full-scale conference with all the participants in their home countries—perhaps even in their own homes.

Global television. This, of course, is the most glamorous, though not necessarily the most important possibility opened up by comsats. The first television satellites were low-powered relay devices whose feeble signals could be picked up only by enormous antenna systems and ultrasensitive receivers. These signals were then amplified a millionfold for rebroadcast. But the time will soon come when we can put high-powered

CANADA'S FIRST
The National Aeronautics and Space Act of 1958 directed, in part, that the U.S. cooperate with foreign nations in space. On September 28, 1962, this cooperation made possible the orbiting of Canada's first spacecraft, Alouette, launched by a U.S. rocket from the West Coast. Alouette, named for a high-flying Canadian lark, gathered data in the ionosphere bearing on the causes of radio interference.

transmitters into orbit, and then every home will be able to tune in directly to broadcasts coming down from space, and international television will become a daily occurrence.

Actually, only three such transmitter satellites would be needed to put at least one television station in broadcasting position for every human being on earth. These transmitter satellites would be placed in a circular "synchronous" orbit at a height of 22,300 miles, so that they would take exactly one day to make a revolution around the earth. From the ground, the satellite would appear to remain in a fixed position in the sky. Such transmitter satellites would be the equivalent of television towers 22,300 miles high, and three of them, spaced evenly around the equator, would blanket the entire globe. And today's static-plagued shortwave radio broadcasts will seem primitive compared with the clear, interference-free reception provided by transmitter satellites.

Communications satellites will probably increase agitation for a basic world language; more realistically, they will perhaps hasten the development of automatic translating devices.

Eye on the earth

Appropriately enough, the world's first operational satellite system designed to transmit practical, everyday information was in the field of meteorology. The highly successful Tiros (Television and Infra Red Observation Satellite) program, commencing in 1960, showed that a camera looking down upon earth from space could provide weather information obtainable in no other way. In 11 weeks of useful life, Tiros I televised 22,952 photos. The meteorologists were no longer confined to a worm's-eye view of the weather; as one of them said, the satellite produced so many photographs, "we've gone from rags to riches overnight."

Tiros I spotted potential hurricanes far out at sea, days before they would have been detected by any other means. It observed the spring breakup of ice in the St. Lawrence River and provided weather forecasts for the resupplying of Antarctic bases. Later Tiros satellites added to these accomplishments with such feats as forecasting the weather for Mercury launchings.

And this was just a start; within a decade, by observing the global weather picture, scientists will at last be able to convert forecasting from an art into a science with great precision. To do so, they must know one vital bit of information: how much heat the earth is receiving from the sun. By heating the atmosphere with its rays, the sun provides the power by which all the world's weather is produced. When the atmosphere is cloudy, much of that power is reflected back into space; when the weather is clear, the energy is trapped and warms land, sea and air —thus producing a totally different weather situation. The extent of the world's cloud cover, therefore, is one of the first facts the meteorologist must know. It can be measured either with thousands of observers or automatically from one satellite.

In a statement issued while he was Chairman of the National Aeronautics and Space Council, Lyndon B. Johnson pointed out that the estimated savings to the United States alone if weather forecasting could be made reliable only five days in advance would be about six billion dollars a year, shared almost equally between agriculture and water-resources management. Over the world as a whole, the saving would be several times as great, and no one can set a value on the lives that would be saved by accurate forecasts and storm warnings. When a global weather satellite system is fully operational, it will pay for the entire cost of a space program considerably more extensive than today's.

From the weather satellite to the military reconnaissance satellite seems only a step, since both are simply looking down on what is going on around the earth. But this step is a very long one. Spotting a camouflaged missile installation, possibly through clouds, is a refinement far outstripping the detection of a hurricane, which may measure up to 1,000 miles in diameter. Furthermore, astronauts have reported that though it is occasionally possible to pick out railroads and highways, sometimes whole cities have proved invisible from space.

Reconnaissance satellites will therefore have to have incredible vision and the ability properly to interpret what they "see." The U.S. has already launched rudimentary reconnaissance satellites (the Midas and Samos series, for example), but it will take time to develop truly reliable satellites to provide the chance of putting President Eisenhower's international reconnaissance "open skies" proposal into effect. If such "open skies" satellites were under the jurisdiction of the United Nations, no one but a potential aggressor could reasonably object to them.

The promise of precision

The very first use ever suggested for an artificial satellite—in the Reverend Edward Everett Hale's 1870 *Brick Moon*—was as an aid to navigation. To fix one's position on our little planet using the existing heavenly bodies is an involved process, requiring some cumbersome mathematics; furthermore, it cannot be practiced in cloudy weather. Although many radio aids to navigation now exist, they all have definite limitations. But a satellite transmitting a radio beacon could serve as a navigational "lighthouse" in even the worst of weather. Such a navigation satellite— Transit—was first launched in 1960, and may point to the day when a radio navigational network will cover the whole earth. Then no one need ever be lost again if he carries a small indicating set which ultimately might be no bigger than that ancient aid, the compass.

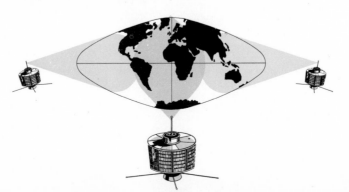

A WORLD-BLANKETING TRIO
Just three satellites, each placed in an orbit exactly the right distance from the earth, could relay telephone and television signals over most of the world. So placed, they would orbit at a speed synchronized to the earth's rotation, thus appearing to hang motionless in the sky, and simplifying the aiming of transmitting and receiving antennas.

103

Closely allied to the navigation satellite is the geodetic, or mapping, satellite, which permits charting of the earth's surface to a much higher degree of precision than has ever been possible before. A geodetic satellite may carry a powerful flashing light, so that when it is photographed streaking across the night sky, it will produce a series of dots against the background of the stars. Ground stations will be able to pinpoint their positions with extreme accuracy by simultaneous observation and calibration of these transmitted flashes.

The foregoing are merely beginnings in the explosively developing field of scientific satellites, which have been launched in dozens and will number in the hundreds by the end of this decade. The ability to put instruments in space has been one of the truly great breakthroughs—to use that overworked phrase accurately, for once—in the history of science. It is necessary to go back to the invention of the telescope, three and a half centuries ago, to find a development of equal importance.

Breaking a barrier

A simple, yet profoundly significant analogy shows why this is so. Imagine a race of intelligent fish that for a long time have been dimly aware —through distorted images glimpsed overhead and by means of objects which occasionally fell into their watery element—that there was another world above the surface of the sea. They have speculated about it for ages, constructing endless theories and formulating philosophies, even theologies. But their real knowledge about the weird realm of dry land is utterly lacking.

Then, suddenly, they invent a periscope and thrust it through the barrier overhead. At once, a new universe is opened up—a universe full of strange creatures and phenomena that it will take them centuries just to record, much less to understand.

A few years after the development of their periscope, these fish take the next step: they build a special vehicle and escape from the sea into the ferociously hostile new element of air. And here, for the first time, they discover fire, electricity, extremes of heat and cold, the behavior of gases —all the things that can never be studied in the sea, and which are the very foundation of science and technology, as we land dwellers know them.

All men until this age have been deep-sea dwellers, unable to see the universe as it really is. Now the time has come to emerge from the ocean of air, to exploit the limitless—and still unimaginable—possibilities of space. For example, the climb of a mere hundred miles up through the atmosphere will make the moon and planets appear 10 times closer. All ground-based telescopes are limited in magnifying power, not by their own optics, but by the incessant shimmering of the unevenly heated air above them. It is very seldom possible to use a power of more than 300

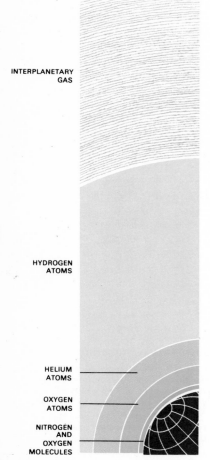

INTERPLANETARY GAS

6,000 MILES

HYDROGEN ATOMS

1,500 MILES

600 MILES

70 MILES

HELIUM ATOMS

OXYGEN ATOMS

NITROGEN AND OXYGEN MOLECULES

A COASTAL CHART OF SPACE
With every foot of altitude, the earth's atmosphere becomes thinner, fading finally into vacuum. The earth's gravity forces the complex mixture of gases to arrange itself into distinct layers, the lighter gases atop the heavier. However, temperature changes induced by the sun cause the thickness of the layers to vary. The altitudes shown in this diagram are, therefore, only approximate.

or 400 on any telescope. Because of atmospheric tremors, the image breaks up, like the dots of a newspaper photograph viewed through a magnifying glass. But above the atmosphere, this shimmering distortion will disappear. With no air intervening, the stars will no longer twinkle, and the images of the planets will hold sharp and steady in the field of the telescope.

Until our own generation, the astronomer had only one source of information about the universe—the rays of visible light. But the rays that the human eye can see cover less than a tiny portion in the spectrum of all possible waves, which extend from gamma rays, sometimes millions of times shorter than light, to radio waves billions of times longer.

Quite recently, the astronomers have opened up a new window on space by observing the universe through the radio waves that it emits, along with all the other sorts of rays. The infant science of radio astronomy has already revealed a cosmos quite different from that disclosed by visible light. If we could observe the heavens by X-rays or gamma rays or short ultraviolet rays, we would see still-different pictures, and we need them all to obtain a full understanding of this diverse universe in which we live.

However, all the short waves from space are completely blocked by the earth's atmosphere. Only instruments in orbit can observe really short waves, and satellites carrying X-ray and ultraviolet detectors have already revealed many surprising and puzzling facts.

Moreover, shining out there among the stars are unknown entities which we have never seen from earth and never will—sources of intense ultraviolet radiation which are, almost literally, too hot to be visible. Only in space—or on the airless moon—will astronomers be able to study them.

Opening new vistas

Before the launching of the first satellites, one thing everybody "knew" about space was that it was empty. It is still empty, as far as human senses are concerned; but we now realize that space is spanned by tenuous bridges of hydrogen gas, sleeted with gusts of high-energy particles and permeated with galaxy-wide magnetic fields. This new knowledge—though only a foretaste of what must come—is already changing our picture of the universe, and giving us fresh clues to its far-off origin in space and time. Questions which once seemed beyond all hope of answer have been settled—only to reveal greater unsuspected problems, as the crest of a hill may open up vistas of new and unsuspected mountain ranges in the blue haze of the distance.

So far most of the information sent back from space has involved highly technical matters, of interest largely to the specialist. Yet out of it will sooner or later come one of those great new syntheses that shake the

A CHARTMAKER

First with balloons, then with rockets, scientists have probed the atmosphere. Explorer XVII was the first satellite designed especially for that purpose. Launched in 1963 into an egg-shaped orbit which carried it through the layer of oxygen atoms and into the helium belt *(opposite)* once every 96 minutes, it repeatedly measured the composition, density, temperature and pressure of the gases that envelop the earth.

souls of men—as Darwin's study of finches in the Galápagos led him to the theory of evolution, and Copernicus' attempts to explain the movements of the planets cast down the earth from the center of the universe. And because knowledge always leads to power, men will one day turn even such obscure and esoteric information as the strength of Jupiter's magnetic field or the pressure at the bottom of Venus' atmosphere to practical use and advantage.

Today, when it costs several thousand dollars to put a pound of payload into orbit, these vast projects are mere dreams. They will remain dreams so long as space travel is in its present primitive state and has to employ monstrous vehicles which are largely destroyed on every flight. (Where would transatlantic travel be even now, if the *Queen Mary*—carrying no passengers and only a three-man crew—sank at the end of every voyage? Saturn V will cost more than 20 times as much as the *Queen Mary*!) What is needed is a vehicle which will make the round trip from earth to orbit and back again intact—that would be refueled after every mission like a conventional airplane.

Once that has been achieved, immense vistas will be opened up. Today, we can no more imagine the research projects and the giant industries that will one day flourish out in space than the fish in our imaginary sea could conceive the possibilities that would be opened up on dry land.

Dividends from the Satellite Patrol

In a few short years man has learned an enormous amount about space—and most of his information has come from the extraordinary firsthand reporters called satellites. To great questing antennas like the one shown opposite, intricately equipped robot patrols have sent back reports on both the dangers and the wonders that lie beyond the newest frontier. Ranging as far as Venus, these wandering investigators have discovered a silent solar wind that blows endlessly through space, a vast pall of radiation around the earth and some surprising information about the shape of our planet. Though they did not even exist as recently as 1956, artificial satellites have now made their influence felt in such practical areas as meteorology, communications, entertainment and even on Wall Street. It is clear that they will be with us for a long time, providing a variety of services so wide-ranging that even experts cannot claim to foresee them all.

GATHERING NEWS FROM SPACE

As a Ranger rocket roars past in a perfect launch, the spiderweb tracery of a 60-foot radio tracking dish begins to follow it, gathering information as long as the rocket remains within range.

From California to England to Australia, similar receivers have relayed a vast amount of data about the solar system and the universe from more than 300 U.S. space probes and satellites.

A WEATHER REPORT FROM VENUS

A measuring device on Mariner II notes the temperature on the surface of Venus. This information, in a number code, is then sent earthward by a three-watt radio transmitter.

Sending the News from Space

A spacecraft is merely useless metal unless it has a mission. One of the most important functions it can serve is to send word back to earth on some of the phenomena it encounters. This is achieved by telemetry, the science of measuring something in one place and reporting the results in another. (The automobile speedometer which measures the wheels' rotation and presents it in miles per hour on the dashboard is a familiar example.) The space age has given telemetry a significance never suspected a few decades ago.

Part of telemetry's task is keeping tabs on the functioning of space equipment. More dramatic is the job of reporting on the environment in which it finds itself. One of its finest successes occurred in December 1962 when Mariner II, after one of the

An antenna catches the signal, reduced in strength to .000,000,000,000,000,000,1 watts.

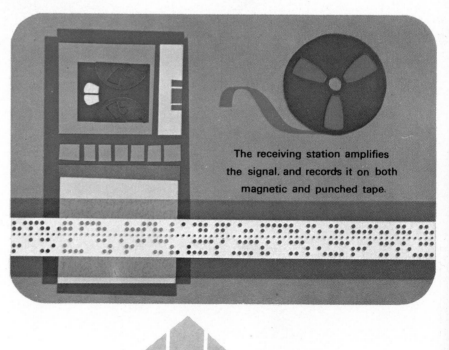

The receiving station amplifies the signal, and records it on both magnetic and punched tape.

longest journeys ever taken by a man-made object, sent back a comprehensive report on Venus. The spacecraft carried 52 sensors to check on its own performance, plus devices assigned to make six kinds of scientific observations—ground temperature, atmosphere temperature, solar wind, radiation, micrometeorites and magnetic forces. It transmitted 65 million units of information 53,900,000 miles.

That treasure trove of information followed a tortuous route from spaceship to scientist. It was transmitted by radio, taken down on tape and wired to computers in the Jet Propulsion Laboratory's Command Center in Pasadena. Then it had to be coded and tabulated before it could be interpreted. The entire sequence is shown in these illustrations, starting at the top of the opposite page.

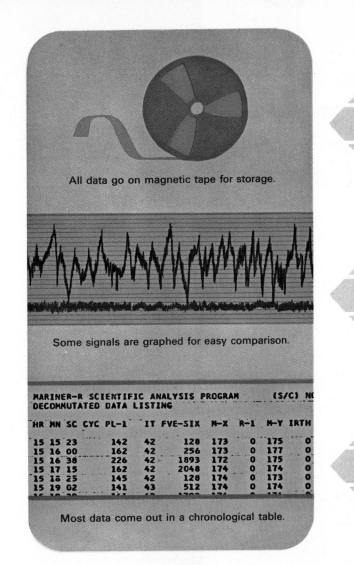

All data go on magnetic tape for storage.

Some signals are graphed for easy comparison.

MARINER-R SCIENTIFIC ANALYSIS PROGRAM								(S/C) N(
DECOMMUTATED DATA LISTING								
HR MN SC	CYC	PL-1	IT	FVE-SIX	M-X	R-1	M-Y	IRTH
15 15 23	142	42		128	173	0	175	0
15 16 00	162	42		256	173	0	177	0
15 16 38	226	42		1893	172	0	175	0
15 17 15	162	42		2048	174	0	174	0
15 18 25	145	42		128	174	0	173	0
15 19 02	141	43		512	174	0	174	0

Most data come out in a chronological table.

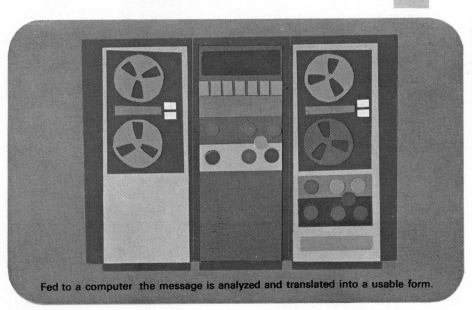

Fed to a computer the message is analyzed and translated into a usable form.

It is then teletyped to headquarters.

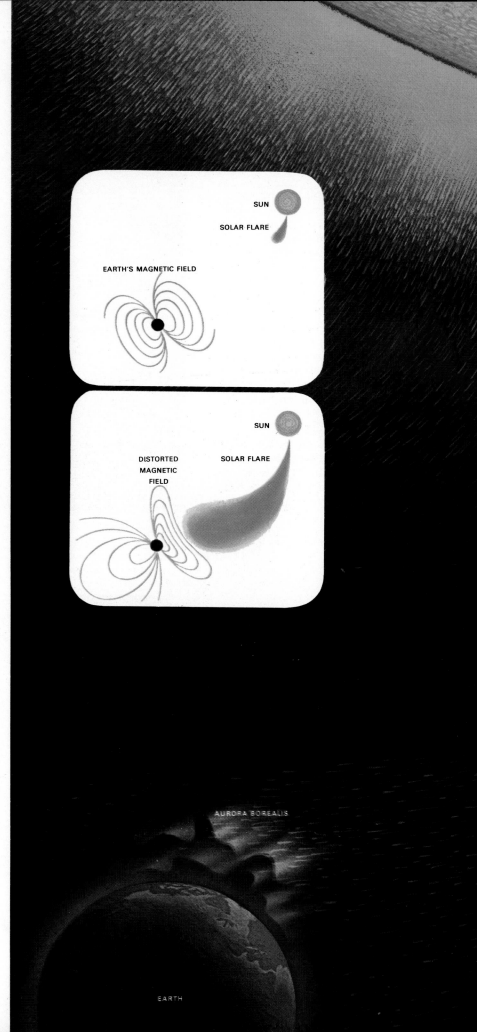

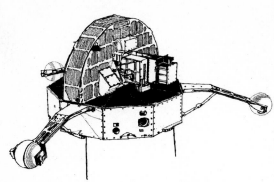

Deadly Storms in Space

The sun, which exerts a vast and generally benign influence on man on earth, will have a much more dangerous effect on him in space. To determine the nature of this solar problem, dozens of rockets and satellites have been sent up on scouting missions. The most important of these is the Orbiting Solar Observatory (OSO).

One of OSO's discoveries concerned the sources of the solar wind, a constant flow of low-energy particles streaming out from the sun. Occasionally, this invisible breath is whipped into storms blowing as fast as 1,000 miles per second. The storms come from violent solar eruptions, called flares (not to be confused with the flamelike "prominences" that also appear on the solar surface). Flares sometimes throw out angry clouds of protons that could be fatal to any astronauts who sailed through them.

The first OSO reported that these destructive spurts are often preceded by microflares not visible from the earth. Hopefully, other OSOs will be able to observe microflares and make regular solar storm forecasts, and so reduce the danger of these deadly disturbances to future travelers in space.

A STORM THAT LIGHTS THE SKY
The insets and large drawing show how a major solar flare erupts above a sunspot area and hurls a storm cloud of charged particles toward the earth. By causing disturbances in the earth's magnetic field, such a cloud can produce the glowing aurora borealis, or northern lights.

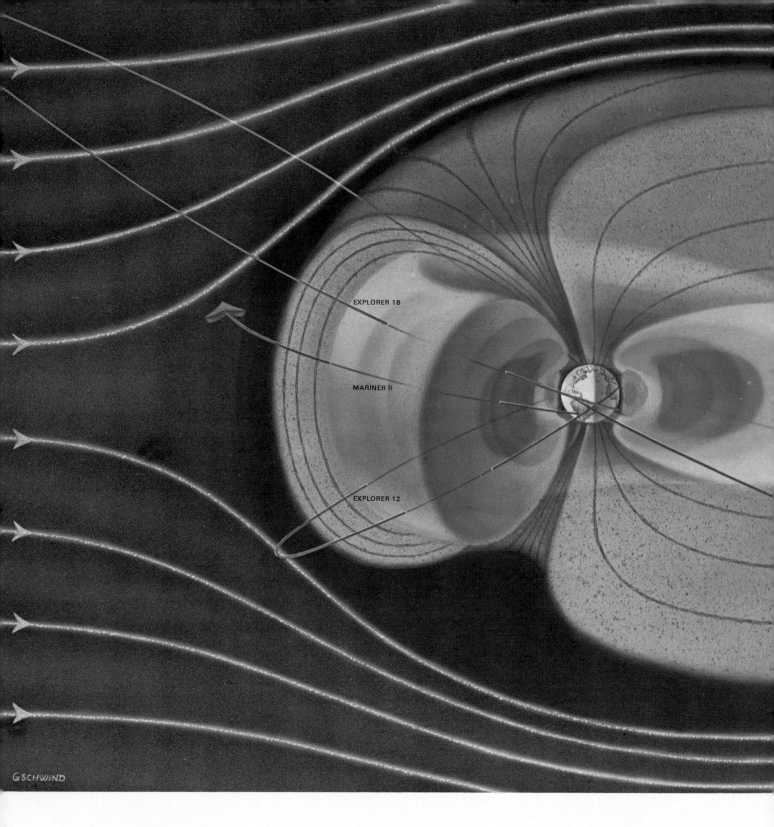

EXPLORER 18

MARINER II

EXPLORER 12

GSCHWIND

An Enveloping Cloak of Radiation

One of the most important discoveries yet made in space was reported by the very first American satellite, Explorer I, in 1958. This satellite (and others since) revealed that several huge layers of radiation particles are trapped by the earth's magnetic field. Called the Van Allen belts after Dr. James Van Allen, who identified them, they extend 50,000 miles toward the sun and, buffeted by the solar wind, trail off some 200,000 miles on the other side of the earth.

Besides their scientific importance, the belts have a highly significant practical implication: they pose the threat of radiation to astronauts as they pass over the doorstep of space.

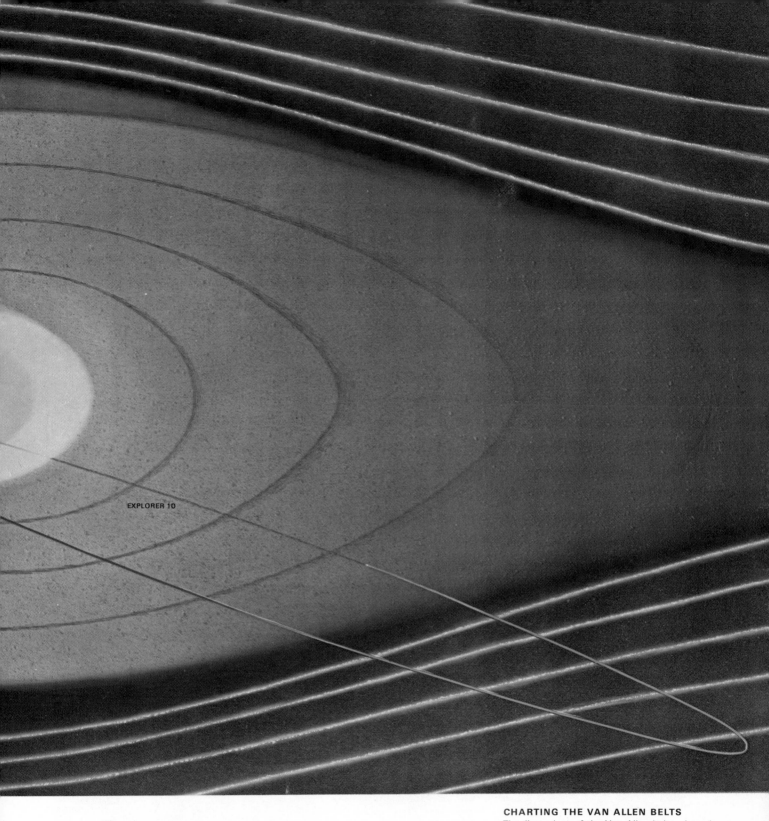

EXPLORER 10

EXPLORER 18

CHARTING THE VAN ALLEN BELTS
The dimensions of the Van Allen belts, shaped by the solar wind *(yellow lines)*, were measured by various Explorer satellites. There are two principal kinds of particles: blue areas indicate concentrations of negative particles (electrons); the orange and pink show positively charged protons. Mariner II's flight to Venus confirmed the solar wind's existence at great distances.

Keeping a Watch on the Weather

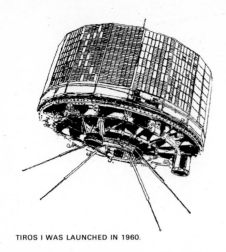

TIROS I WAS LAUNCHED IN 1960.

Much of North America's weather has its inception in remote corners of the globe. Tiros, Nimbus and other satellites have spied out this incipient weather, so it can no longer catch its victims by surprise.

In September 1961, for instance, Tiros III sent TV pictures of a storm brewing in the Atlantic. Within days the biggest evacuation in U.S. history had saved 350,000 Gulf Coast inhabitants from Hurricane Carla. Such coverage, plus information Tiros provides on heat radiation from clouds, earth and ocean (below), may one day help men realize an ancient dream: they can stop talking about the weather and do something about it.

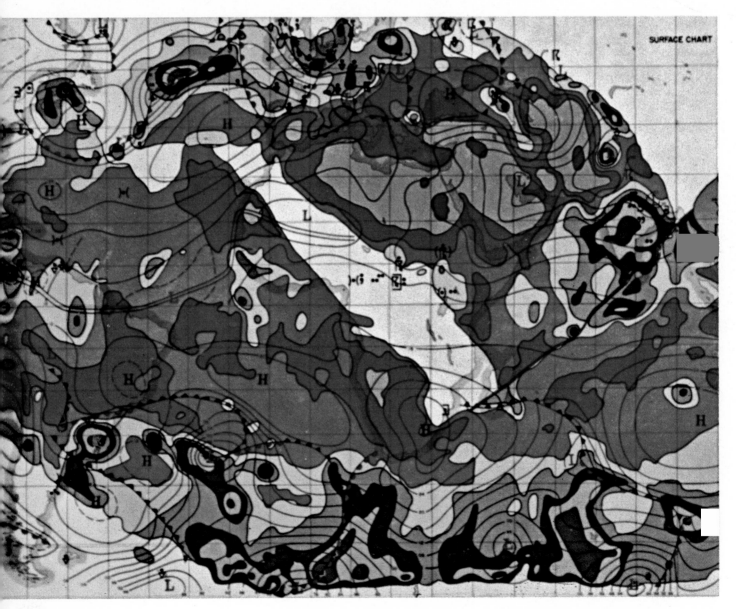

PUTTING THE HEAT ON THE MAP

This weather map reflects data sent from special Tiros sensors which record the amount of heat radiated by the earth's surface and the clouds. The color coding, over a map which has South America at left and Southeast Asia at right, shows cool, cloudy areas in green and blue, hot, clear areas in pink and red. At right center is a cluster of monsoon clouds over India.

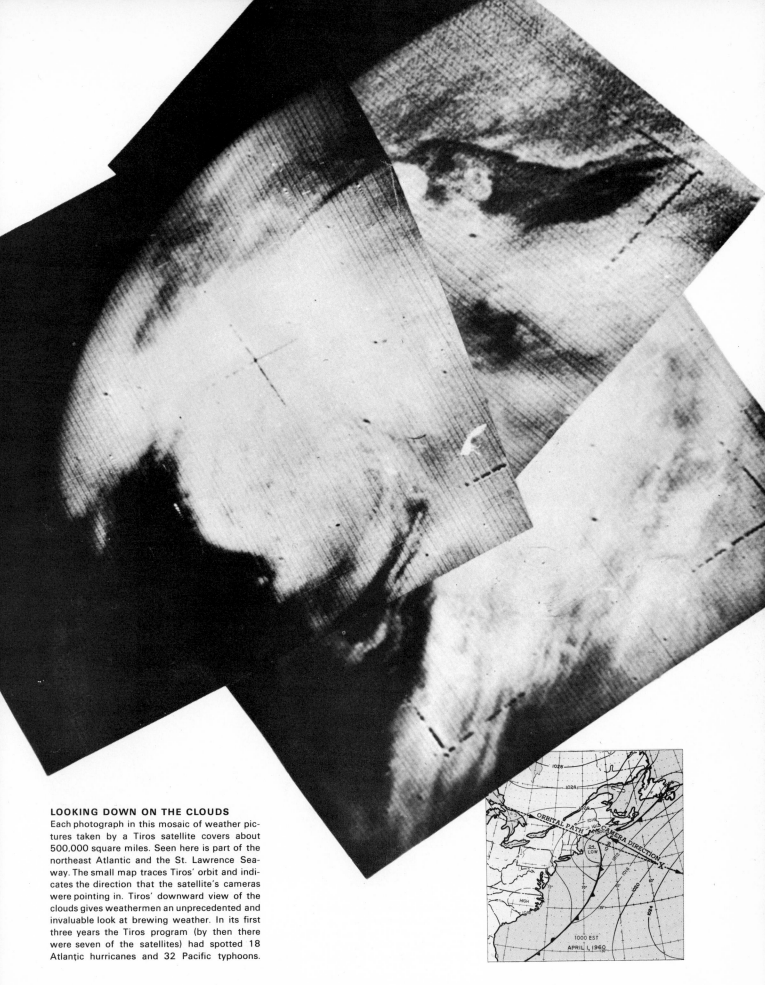

LOOKING DOWN ON THE CLOUDS

Each photograph in this mosaic of weather pictures taken by a Tiros satellite covers about 500,000 square miles. Seen here is part of the northeast Atlantic and the St. Lawrence Seaway. The small map traces Tiros' orbit and indicates the direction that the satellite's cameras were pointing in. Tiros' downward view of the clouds gives weathermen an unprecedented and invaluable look at brewing weather. In its first three years the Tiros program (by then there were seven of the satellites) had spotted 18 Atlantic hurricanes and 32 Pacific typhoons.

115

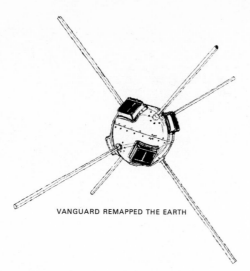

VANGUARD REMAPPED THE EARTH

A New Look for the Earth

For centuries scientists have thought of the earth as an oblate spheroid—a sphere slightly flattened at the ends, like an orange. Now it develops that it has something of a pear shape as well. A remarkable discovery stemming from the flight of Vanguard I in 1958 has proved that the earth is narrower on top and wider at the hips than had been believed.

Although the new bulges are barely perceptible *(diagram below)*, the difference is enough to be significant. The oblate-spheroid theory presupposed the earth to be a somewhat plastic mass that responded to gravity and rotation by assuming a flattened form. The new discovery means the earth must be structurally firmer than geodesists had thought, a development that will have far-reaching effects on their investigations.

The discovery was made by Dr. John O'Keefe *(right)* after a colleague had noticed minor but unexpected aberrations in Vanguard's path. A satellite's orbit depends on the earth's gravity. If the satellite follows an irregular path, there must be irregularity in the pull of gravity—which, in turn, indicates an irregularity in the earth's mass, for it is mass that determines gravity. O'Keefe decided that Vanguard's strange course indicated an odd-shaped earth—and from the satellite's route he worked out earth's new look. It has since been confirmed by other satellites.

50 FEET

25 FEET · 25 FEET

25 FEET · 25 FEET

50 FEET

A SMALL BUT IMPORTANT BULGE
In the drawing at left the blue line gives an exaggerated picture of the earth's true shape: slightly elongated north of the equator, with a small bulge south of it. The difference, although scientifically significant, is infinitesimal compared with earth's 7,927-mile diameter.

FOLLOWING VANGUARD'S CLUES
Dr. John O'Keefe, NASA astronomer and geodesist, pores over a computer tabulation used in satellite tracking. Another NASA scientist, Mrs. Ann E. Bailie, first noticed Vanguard's clues to the globe's irregular shape; it was Dr. O'Keefe who figured out what they meant.

116

TELSTAR, THE TV COMSAT

A Bullish Future for Comsats

On June 3, 1964, man's vision of utilizing space for his practical ends became a matter-of-fact business reality when 10 million shares of stock in the Communications Satellite Corporation were offered for public sale. No longer was there any doubt of the feasibility of using satellites for worldwide communications.

The communications satellite was first suggested in 1945 by Arthur C. Clarke, who wrote the text of this book. Score, the first primitive "comsat," went up in 1958; increasingly complex satellites followed. One of the most spectacular was the Telstar I, which first relayed live TV pictures across the Atlantic in June 1962. Television signals travel only in a straight line; radio signals can be badly distorted over long distances. Telstar served as a relay tower which could receive signals beamed from an earth station like the one at right and pass them along loud and clear. Once Telstar was in orbit, it was only a matter of time before there would be enough comsats on station to bring virtually every part of the globe into electronic hailing distance.

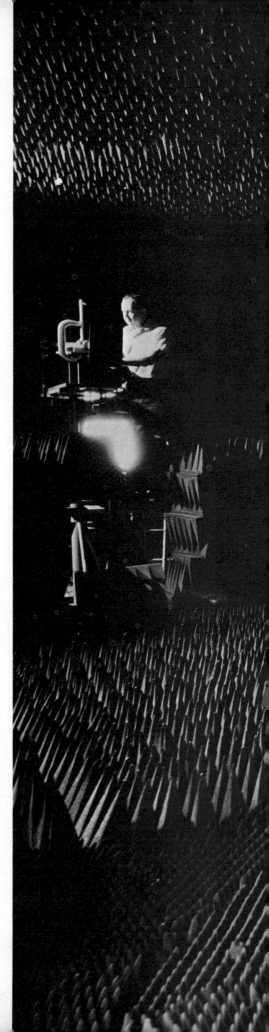

COMMAND HEADQUARTERS
Signals for U.S. communications satellites are beamed from this structure in Andover, Maine. Inside the inflated plastic-and-rubber balloon stands a 94-foot-high antenna which transmits and receives telephone and television signals relayed by comsats like Telstar and Early Bird.

A RADIO-PROOF TEST CHAMBER
Aiming a radio beam at the Comsat Corporation's first satellite, Early Bird, a technician in a Hughes Aircraft Company laboratory checks the Bird's transmitter-receiver system. Precisely aligned wedges of spongy foam eliminate stray radio waves to simulate the total silence of space.

6

The Challenge
of the
Lunar Decade

*Space is clearly the great breakthrough of human knowledge
—for centuries to come. . . . We have a long and undistin-
guished record of America failing to anticipate the promise
and potential of each new age of science, invention and discovery. . . . Even so far-sighted an American as Woodrow Wilson spent time denouncing the automobile. The steamboat, the
locomotive, the airplane, all brought prophecies of doom and
gloom. We have learned a lesson we surely do not need to be
taught again.*

—LYNDON B. JOHNSON, *June 1963*

OUR CURRENT VIEW OF THE MOON is distorted by an unavoidable but
transient fact of history. Because the moon is incomparably nearer than
any other heavenly body, it will be man's first target beyond the earth.
Yet it represents much less than one thousandth of the explorable
land in the solar system, and there are other celestial bodies of far
greater promise and interest. To imagine, therefore, that the moon is
the final goal of astronautics is ludicrously shortsighted—to imagine
that this goal is merely a trophy in a cosmic race between two mid-
20th Century powers, almost blindness.

On the moon, less than two seconds away at the speed of light, we
shall test and perfect the techniques needed to explore more distant—
and often more dangerous—worlds. Whether we succeed or fail on our
single natural satellite will shape the future of astronautics for years
to come.

Some early theoreticians of space flight realized that, with chemical
fuels, it would be extremely difficult to make a manned landing on the
moon and a safe return to earth. Indeed, some felt that it was impossible and that such missions would have to await the advent of nuclear
rocket propulsion.

It is hard enough to set down a reasonable payload gently on the surface of the moon; but if that payload has to be brought back to earth,
it must also carry fuel for the return journey. This makes the problem
many, many times as difficult as the one-way voyage. There would be
little transatlantic flying even today if airliners could not refuel at their
destinations. It will be a long time before we can refuel on the moon
—though that will come.

Most technical problems have more than one solution; the lunar
round trip has at least three. The first is what might be called the brute-
force method; it involves building a single gigantic vehicle which would
take off from earth, go directly to the moon, land there and still have
enough fuel for the return journey. At lift-off from earth, such a rocket

POWER PLANT FOR A MOON SHOT
Crouched under globular fuel and oxygen tanks
on a test stand at Edwards Air Force Base in
California is the mighty F-1 engine, part of the
Apollo moon project's power plant. Five F-1's,
each generating one and a half million pounds
of thrust, team up in the first stage of Apollo's
Saturn V booster. A single F-1 engine consumes
fuel at the same rate as 600,000 automobiles.

(assuming a three-man crew) might even weigh 40 million pounds. (By comparison, the Atlas, which seemed so impressive when it blasted the first American astronauts into orbit, weighs a mere 265,000 pounds.)

Such a monster could be built, but there are more elegant—and more economical—ways of achieving the same results. They all depend, in some way or other, upon the idea of a rendezvous between two or more rockets in space. The rendezvous can be in an orbit around the earth or in one around the moon.

The notion of orbital rendezvous, like so many other space ideas, stems from Hermann Oberth's 1923 book, *The Rocket into Interplanetary Space*. Oberth pointed out that once a rocket had been safely established in orbit, refueling and resupply operations could be carried out by sending other rockets into the same orbit. The whole concept is very similar to that of flight-refueling in the air, which is now a standard procedure for long-range bomber and fighter operations.

However, there is a most important difference. An aircraft cannot remain aloft indefinitely while it waits for a flying tanker to make contact. But a spacecraft in orbit can do precisely this. After launching, it might be repaired, tested—even rebuilt—over a period of weeks or months before a tanker was sent up to refuel it. This gives Earth Orbit Rendezvous operations a great degree of flexibility; mistakes can be corrected, and delays in launching subsequent vehicles are not necessarily serious setbacks. The U.S. lunar project, however, will utilize a different kind of orbit, known as Lunar Orbit Rendezvous (LOR), based on the use of a special type of spacecraft for the most crucial phase of the mission—actual landing on the moon.

An impossible vehicle

All terrestrial transport vehicles are highly specialized. Consider, for example, the different functions of family runabout, Jeep, bulldozer, heavy truck and racing car. It would be impossible to design a single vehicle replacing all of these, and ridiculous even to try.

In the same way, a lunar round trip involves so many widely differing conditions of gravity and air resistance that a single vehicle able to cope with all of them would be a designer's nightmare. This becomes obvious as soon as one lists the tasks it would have to perform.

First, it must fight its way up through the atmosphere, carrying a very heavy payload, while earth's gravity attempts to pull it back. It must thus have engines developing hundreds of tons of thrust. But for the landing on the moon and the subsequent return to earth a much more modest power plant will suffice, because lunar gravity is only one sixth of earth's.

For the lunar landing, there is no need for streamlining or for heavy heat shields to provide protection from frictional heating, since all operations are in a complete vacuum. Yet, for the very last stage of the journey—the final 100-mile descent through the earth's atmosphere, at the end of a half-million-mile round trip—an immensely strong and heavy heat shield is essential, or the vehicle will be burned up on re-entry. To carry this shield all the way to the moon and back would involve an appalling waste of fuel and a great increase in the initial takeoff weight.

By stages to the moon

The answer to the problem was given in a series of papers published in the late 1940s by the British Interplanetary Society. The ideal solution was to use a different vehicle for each stage of the journey. Thus a powerful, short-range rocket, perhaps with stubby wings for the glide back into the atmosphere, would be used to carry supplies and equipment up to the orbit around the earth and to bring back returning travelers. It would be designed for the first and most difficult part of any space journey—but it would never climb more than a few hundred miles from earth, or attain orbital speed of more than 18,000 miles an hour.

The second type of spaceship would be a lightweight, low-powered vehicle since it would never have to withstand high accelerations or the tremendous forces of atmospheric re-entry. In fact, it would never land anywhere, but would ferry cargo back and forth from earth orbit to lunar orbit.

Finally, the actual descent to the moon would be the job of yet a third vehicle. The lunar landing craft would have motors of modest power, to counteract the moon's gravity during descent and takeoff, and would be fitted with a shock-absorbing undercarriage to take up the final impact of touchdown.

This triple-vehicle moon journey would involve a very high degree of sophistication. Our space program will have to make do with only two vehicles and somewhat lower efficiency—at a corresponding gain in simplicity and, perhaps, reliability. The Apollo project will use two primary vehicles; one will make the journey from earth to an orbit round the moon and back again, while the second—known as the Lunar Excursion Module, called the LEM—will make the brief hop down to the lunar surface and back to the orbiting mother ship. It will carry only two of the three-man crew. One astronaut will remain in orbit. He can supervise operations—and if anything goes wrong on the moon, he at least will have a chance of making a safe return.

When his companions rejoin him, after a day or two on the moon, the LEM will be abandoned in lunar orbit, and the mother ship will head

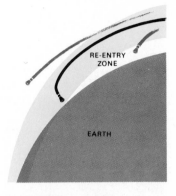

RETURNING FROM ORBIT
To return to earth, an orbiting Mercury capsule is first slowed by retro-rockets, then is eased down in a smooth arc *(middle path)* by adjusting the angle at which its blunt nose burrows into the atmosphere. Too shallow an angle leaves it in orbit *(top)*; too steep an angle plunges it at high speed into the crushing wall of dense lower air *(bottom path)*.

RETURNING FROM THE MOON
An Apollo capsule approaching the earth after its round trip to the moon will be traveling too fast to make an immediate re-entry. Instead of using retro-rockets, the capsule will be slowed by skipping in and out of the dense layers of atmosphere. This maneuver will also place it on the proper trajectory for it to make an accurate on-target landing.

back to earth. Final re-entry through the earth's atmosphere will be carried out in a conical, blunt-ended vehicle rather like an enlarged Mercury capsule.

The giant Saturn V, heart of the Apollo program, for all its size, power and technical intricacy is merely the lunar bus. The actual flight will be relatively unimportant, and probably uneventful. All that really matters is what the passengers do when they arrive at their destination.

The wonders that await us

So much has been written about the moon, and so many thousands of lunar touchdowns have occurred in films and fiction, that one sometimes wonders if the real M-Day may be an anticlimax. But that possibility is very remote. Though we may think we already know a great deal about the moon, our ignorance is still monumental. We will be enlightened somewhat by the landings of robot Rangers, Luniks and Surveyors, but no machine can compete with human eyes and brains actually on the spot. A robot can never be programmed to deal with the unexpected, and the universe is bound to be full of surprises. The most interesting things we will find on the moon are precisely those that we cannot anticipate today.

There is more to the moon than is generally realized. For one thing, it is about the size of both Americas combined. Such an area will take many years (and perhaps many lives) to explore in detail. Though it will be mapped at high speed beforehand by orbiting satellites, the slow-moving prospector with the geologist's hammer will be the real investigator. And the surface exploration of the moon will be greatly facilitated and terribly handicapped by the literally unearthly conditions that prevail there.

The fact that explorers must wear pressure suits and carry their own supplies of oxygen puts a great strain on the logistics of any lunar operation. In all the thousands of years that they have been traveling over the earth's surface, men have never been confronted with regions where they could not breathe. Even in the thin atmosphere at the top of Mount Everest, a trained climber can work and survive for considerable periods without artificial aids; an astronaut would last only seconds in the lunar vacuum.

However, the absence of an atmosphere is not an unmixed evil. Among other things, it means that the moon has no weather. It is extremely difficult for us, accustomed to cloud and fog, wind and rain, to imagine the total absence of these atmospheric phenomena. None of the meteorological variations that make life interesting, unpredictable and occasionally impossible on the earth ever takes place on the moon. There is only the regular and utterly unvarying cycle of lunar night and day. A

A WHIMSICAL POKE IN THE EYE

A pockmarked man in the moon looks askance at a spaceship, which landed in his eye in the 1902 science-fiction movie *A Trip to the Moon*. The movie satirized dreams of space travel. Its bullet-shaped spaceship was launched by cannon, a la Jules Verne, and the top-hatted scientists inside found the moon inhabited by devils and dragons.

century in advance, one can state confidently that the thermometer at lunar noon in a certain spot will touch 250°F.—and that at midnight 15 days later it will plunge to 250°F. below zero. These extremes, though they outrange any found on earth, will not be difficult to handle by properly protected astronauts in the perfectly insulating vacuum of space; they present far less of a menace than antarctic blizzard or tropical hurricane. Plain weather has probably frustrated and killed more mariners and explorers than any other single factor; the men on the moon will have many problems, but this will not be among them.

Because the moon turns very slowly on its axis, its day is almost 30 times as long as ours. Consequently, the sharp-edged frontier between night and day, which moves at 1,000 miles an hour on the earth's equator, has a maximum speed of about 10 miles an hour on the moon. Although on earth only a jet can keep up with the sun, in high lunar latitudes a walking man could do it with little exertion.

The most interesting and best-known consequence of the moon's slow rotation is that its day has become synchronized with its orbital period around the earth, so that it always keeps the same hemisphere turned toward us. In the remote past the moon rotated more rapidly, but the drag of the tides induced in its once-plastic body by the more massive earth robbed it of its spin. (The moon is reciprocating, and is very gradually slowing down the earth's rotation. However, by the time the moon succeeds in completely stopping the earth's rotation, the entire solar system will be drastically altered, and life on earth will have ceased to be.)

The waterless "seas"

Until the advent of Lunik III and Zond III, astronomers felt frustrated by the fact that they were unable to observe almost a whole hemisphere of the very closest body in space. However, there was never any reason to suppose that the far side of the moon would differ fundamentally from the one that we can observe, and the photographs made by the Soviet satellites bear this out. Moreover, in a generation or so, that hidden land may be a scientific asset of the very greatest importance. The moon's low gravity, its slow rotation and the total absence of wind all combine to make the moon an ideal site for really large radio telescopes. Such a telescope, positioned in the exact center of the far side, would have the whole bulk of the moon—2,160 miles of solid rock—between it and the ever-increasing electronic racket of earth.

There is, of course, no water on the moon, and it is perhaps unfortunate that such terms as "sea," "lake," "bay" and "ocean"—bestowed by the first lunar map makers more than 300 years ago—are still in general use. But we seem stuck with them, and the Russians have now christened a Bay of Astronauts and a Moscow Sea on the far side of the moon.

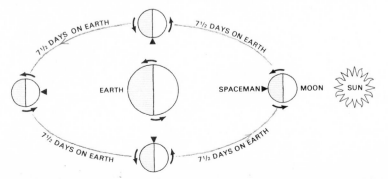

A LONG DAY'S JOURNEY

A spaceman who remains in a fixed spot on the moon *(black triangle)* will see the sun rise and set only once a month. While 30 days are passing on earth, the moon circles the earth once, meanwhile spinning once on its axis. To the spaceman, the earth will show phases: at "midnight" on the moon, a spaceman would see a "full earth."

These aqueous names have been applied to the areas which through the telescope appear dark and relatively flat. However, close examination shows that they are full of ridges, hills and small craters, and the impression of uniformity may be wholly misleading. Even in the most favorable circumstances, it is not possible to see objects on the moon much smaller than half a mile across; thus even the huge Pentagon building might be below the limit of visibility if it were on the moon, although its shadow at dawn or sunset would be quite conspicuous.

In the past there has been considerable difference of opinion among the experts concerning the precise nature of the lunar surface. Evidence from optical and radio telescopes, reflected radar waves and even photographs taken right on the moon have not settled the conflict of theories.

Some scientists have contended that the lunar surface is made up mostly of hard rock; others held that it is rather like the back of an angry porcupine. Mild alarm was created by a hypothesis which explained the relatively flat "seas" as giant dust bowls that over the eons had collected material eroded from the surrounding mountains. Into this dust, it was gloomily asserted, a descending spaceship would sink without a trace.

Whatever the truth (and final agreement may not come until man has returned with his first samples of the moon's surface), experts will undoubtedly find means by which vehicles and explorers can operate with relative ease on the lunar surface. Finding the safest areas for these activities is one of the main tasks of Surveyor and Lunik probes. If the dark "seas" and "oceans" present too many difficulties, the light-colored mountainous highlands may turn out to be more hospitable.

Those illusory mountains

Some of the lunar mountains are more than 20,000 feet high, but certain photographs and artists' illustrations give the extremely misleading impression that the moon is a place of towering cliffs and yawning canyons. The most dramatic lunar photographs taken from the earth—and therefore most frequently published—are taken near dawn or dusk, when the slanting sunlight grossly exaggerates every difference of level. At such a time, a crater whose walls are actually about as precipitous as a beginner's ski slope may look like a steep-sided funnel. The truth is that few lunar gradients can match the slopes of San Francisco, and in a gravity only a sixth of the earth's, the mountains and craters of the moon will present very little obstacle to exploration.

Yet a gentle incline—or even a flat plain—may be almost impassable for an unprepared astronaut. Because the moon has no atmosphere, there has been no erosion or weathering—at least none by water and wind, as on earth—and some areas may contain small, sharp-edged obstacles like stilettos or razor blades of rock. Heaven help an explorer who tries to

A MOUNTAINOUS MISCONCEPTION
Ever since Galileo's first telescopic glimpse of the moon, scientists have known that the lunar surface has many enormous mountains. Because earth's mountains are steep until weathering erodes them, it was assumed that mountains on the moon would be like the steep-sided peaks shown here. The reasoning: there could be no weathering since the moon has no atmosphere.

scramble across a sheet of the volcanic glass called obsidian, which makes very good natural knives.

Perhaps nowhere is present scientific opinion more divided than in the case of the origin of the lunar craters. These are the most characteristic features of the moon's surface. They range in size from pits less than a mile across to craters well over 100 miles in diameter. For more than a century astronomers have been bitterly divided concerning their origin. Many scientists are certain that the lunar craters were caused by the impact of giant meteors, while others believe that they are of internal, or volcanic, origin. It will be amusing if both sides turn out to be wrong, but it is more likely that both of them will turn out to be at least partially right.

The lost story of the universe

What is certain, however, is that on the moon we will find waiting for us five billion years of history profoundly different from that of the planet Earth. The face of the moon may have carried down the ages, virtually untouched by time, a record of conditions that existed when the universe itself was young. On earth, all such records have long ago been erased by wind, rain and other geological forces. When we reach the moon, it will be as if an entire library of lost volumes is suddenly thrown open to us.

Until very recently, the moon was regarded as a completely dead region. Though some observers (mostly amateurs—few professional astronomers bothered to look at the moon) had reported local mists and the collapse of one small crater, no one took them very seriously. Then in 1958, the Russian astronomer N. A. Kozyrev claimed to have observed an outburst of gas from a peak in the 70-mile-wide crater Alphonsus, and he also took a spectrogram indicating the presence of carbon there. More recently, bright, temporary glows have been reported by U.S. Air Force observers engaged in mapping the moon.

After a good deal of initial skepticism, since his report was at variance with almost all preconceived ideas, Kozyrev's findings were accepted by many leading astronomers. The presence on the moon of carbon—the basic element of life—raises several interesting possibilities. Perhaps, in the very remote past, the moon may have had a fairly extensive atmosphere, and even real seas instead of today's misnamed ocean features. Life of some kind may have evolved there long before it appeared on earth. There may have been countless fantastic forms, which later passed away, leaving strange fossils for the geologists of the future to uncover.

This in itself would be of enormous interest and importance, but it is also conceivable that some of these hypothetical lunar life-forms may

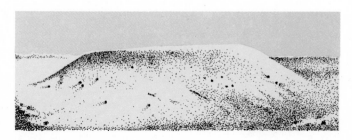

THE PLAIN TRUTH

Continued observation and refined techniques of measurement now indicate that while the moon does indeed have enormous mountains *(opposite page)*, very few of them are steep-sided, as was once believed. Instead these lunar mountains tend to slope gradually, as shown here, with grades seldom steeper than a 10° angle. Precipitous slopes have been eroded by meteorites.

have been able to adapt themselves to the slow loss of atmosphere and the increasing severity of the temperature. Even now, a few yards underground or in the neighborhood of still slightly active craters like Alphonsus, free water and sporadic traces of atmosphere may exist, producing a local "microclimate" in which some hardy forms of life could survive. This may not be at all probable, but many biologists agree that it is possible.

Any contamination of the moon by terrestrial bacteria, preventing experts from identifying "aboriginal" lunar organisms, would be a major scientific disaster. For this reason, the Ranger space probes were carefully sterilized, and it is believed that this process may have damaged electronic components, causing the failure of several missions. However, it is better to lose a few robots and a few years of time than to risk destroying knowledge that can never be replaced.

Tapping the lunar riches

Lifeless or not, the moon will keep armies of scientists busy for generations, and the discoveries flowing back to earth will enrich human culture in countless ways. Almost everything that is true of industries and laboratories in orbit will be applicable to the moon as well; but the moon will have at least one immeasurable advantage over any space station. It can provide an unlimited supply of raw materials.

The moon consists of the same elements as the earth, though they will doubtless occur in different combinations. Many familiar substances, such as oil, coal and lime, will almost certainly be missing, since these are the products of abundant life over eons of time. But the chemical and mining engineers will find alternatives; the nuclear engineers will provide the power. Closed communities could be set up on the moon, recycling their oxygen and water, growing crops (which will not only provide food but will also purify the air) during the two-week "days" of fierce, unbroken sunlight.

Perhaps these lunar settlements will never contain more than a few hundred scientists, and will bear a close resemblance to the bases we have set up in the Antarctic. But it is much more likely that as our technical resources increase, these communities will grow until they cover areas many square miles in extent. Three hundred years from now, there may be committees trying desperately to save the last unspoiled fragments of the lunar wilderness.

But why should we wish to live on the moon—even if we can make it habitable? In the first case, it is not a question of conscious wishing. The human species has always moved into new territory as soon as it became technically possible. The march of civilization, as the geographer Ellsworth Huntington has pointed out, has been mainly "Coldward and

Stormward." Huntington contends that the more hostile the environment, the greater the ingenuity required to cope with it, and the higher the level of the resulting culture. This, of course, is a variation of Toynbee's famous "Challenge and Response" thesis; and undeniably space now provides mankind with the sort of challenge which, in the very near future, will no longer be found on this shrinking earth.

Such metaphysical arguments cut little ice with the sort of critic of narrow vision who prides himself on being a hardheaded, practical businessman, with his feet firmly on the ground. He is always with us. A century ago he was shouting "Seward's Folly!" as the Secretary of State proposed to buy, for $7,200,000, the half-million-square-mile chunk of useless snow and ice known as Russian America, now the state of Alaska. Just as we find this shortsighted, our grandchildren will doubtless find it incredible that anyone ever doubted the necessity for colonizing the moon. Yet, before the dawn of lunar exploration we can only guess at reasons why this should be so.

If nothing else, the moon will provide a superb staging area for journeys to the planets. It is a kind of stepping-stone in space. The energy needed to get off its surface is less than one twentieth of that needed to escape from earth. Thus the moon has an enormous advantage as a supply base for interplanetary flights—provided, of course, that we can find suitable materials there for building space vehicles. This is one of the reasons why the development of lunar technology and industry will be so important. Once we can refuel vehicles from the moon, rather than from the earth, the cost of earth-moon operations will be reduced by an enormous percentage. It will no longer be necessary to build—and jettison—rockets weighing many thousands of tons in order to land a few tons of payload on the moon. Space flight will emerge from its present status as a fantastically expensive stunt, and will start to make economic—and ultimately commercial—sense.

A slingshot in space

Even refueling on the moon, however, might be only a beginning. The fact that it has no atmosphere and a relatively low escape velocity may allow us to develop a launching technique much more economical than rocket propulsion. This is the old idea of the "space gun" made famous by Jules Verne. This scheme would not involve a gun in the literal sense, powered by explosives, but rather an electrically powered horizontal launching track like the catapults used on aircraft carriers. To shoot man-carrying vehicles off the moon at an acceptable acceleration, this launching track would have to be at least 20 miles long and would obviously be a major piece of engineering. But it would make the return trip to earth possible without the use of rocket fuel, except a

SURVIVAL FROM SUN AND ROCK

This equipment may provide moon visitors with food, water, air and power. The procedure is based on the assumption that lunar rocks contain water in their crystal structure. Sunlight is focused on these rocks until they become so hot they give off steam—which contains not only water (H_2O) but carbon dioxide (CO_2) and nitrogen (N_2). The carbon dioxide, with sunlight, makes possible photosynthesis, which allows growth of green plants as food. Photosynthesis also produces oxygen (O_2), which mixes with the nitrogen to form a synthetic air. As by-products of the process, the steam can be used to drive a turbine for electric power, and further heating of the lunar rocks might produce hydrogen for use as a rocket propellant.

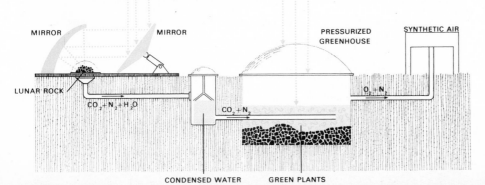

SUNLIGHT   SUNLIGHT

MIRROR   MIRROR   PRESSURIZED   SYNTHETIC AIR
                                GREENHOUSE

LUNAR ROCK O_2+N_2

$CO_2+N_2+H_2O$ CO_2+N_2

CONDENSED WATER   GREEN PLANTS

very small quantity for navigational purposes. The electric power for the catapult would be provided by fixed, nuclear-powered generators. We would then have, in effect, the equivalent of an electric railroad from moon to earth.

William Escher, working for NASA's Future Projects Office, christened this lunar rail-launch device the "Lunatron," and investigated its theoretical operation in considerable detail. The Lunatron would have many possible uses; it could even shoot supplies of moon-produced rocket fuel into rendezvous orbits around the earth, for the refueling of outward-bound spacecraft.

Whether such techniques are ever necessary depends upon the rate at which space-propulsion systems are developed. In the exploration of the solar system, the moon may play a role similar to that of the airports at Shannon and Gander in transatlantic aviation. They were vital in the early days, but eventually they were bypassed as a result of technological improvements. Yet, as far as one can look into the future, this giant satellite so close at hand will be one of our most valuable assets scientifically, industrially—even emotionally. For the time will come, perhaps sooner than we think, when to thousands of men it will be the only home they ever know. And on the moon, to borrow William Faulkner's words, we will not merely survive; we will prevail.

To the Moon: Landmark of Space Travel

As distances in space are measured, the moon is not far away—a mere 240,000 miles. But getting there has required a mobilization of energies and talents hitherto unequaled. An estimated $20 billion, 20,000 companies and 300,000 workers have been committed to putting Americans on the moon. At first the lunar program, called Project Apollo, faced baffling riddles: Could the human organism be shielded from all the hazards of space? Was it possible to perform a rendezvous in orbit? Could a heavy vehicle land on the lunar surface? Long before all the answers were in, the equipment was being designed and built. At Cape Kennedy construction proceeded on the world's largest building (*opposite*) to house the moon rocket. Elsewhere men worked on ways to go and on machines to operate in the lunar void. While Apollo planners hurried to make possible a landing before 1970, others looked further ahead—to lunar visits of two years or more.

ONE BRIGHT AND FUTURE DAY
Some time before 1970 the Saturn V rocket will emerge from its hangar, which is half again the volume of the Pentagon. Atop a truck half the size of a football field, the rocket will begin the slowest leg of man's voyage to the moon—a one-mile-an-hour crawl to the launch pad. The 3,000-ton spaceship will carry a "payload" of less than 500 pounds—the weight of three intrepid men.

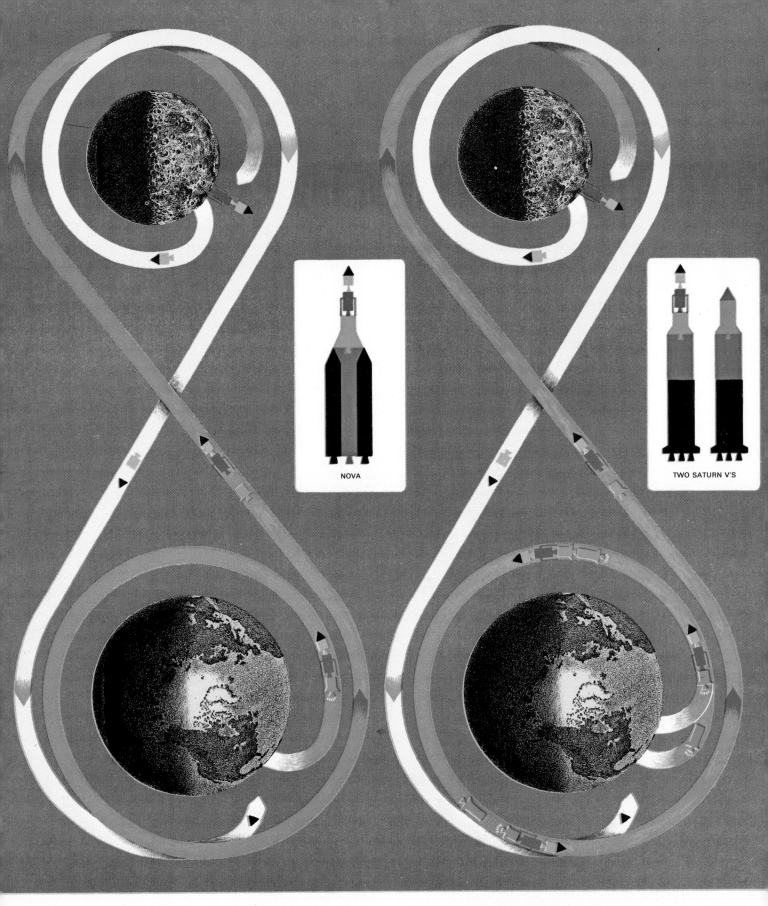

NOVA

TWO SATURN V'S

DIRECT FLIGHT
Under this plan, one huge rocket would hoist the Apollo craft, along with its lunar landing stage *(red)*, directly from earth to moon. The craft would then back to a landing. Part of the landing stage *(yellow)* would later boost the capsule *(black)* back into space for the return.

EARTH ORBIT RENDEZVOUS
This proposal provided for two Saturn V's—one carrying the Apollo capsule and its lunar landing stages—that would rendezvous in an orbit around the earth. One Saturn would then replenish the other's empty tanks with a load of propellant carried in a special unit *(green)*.

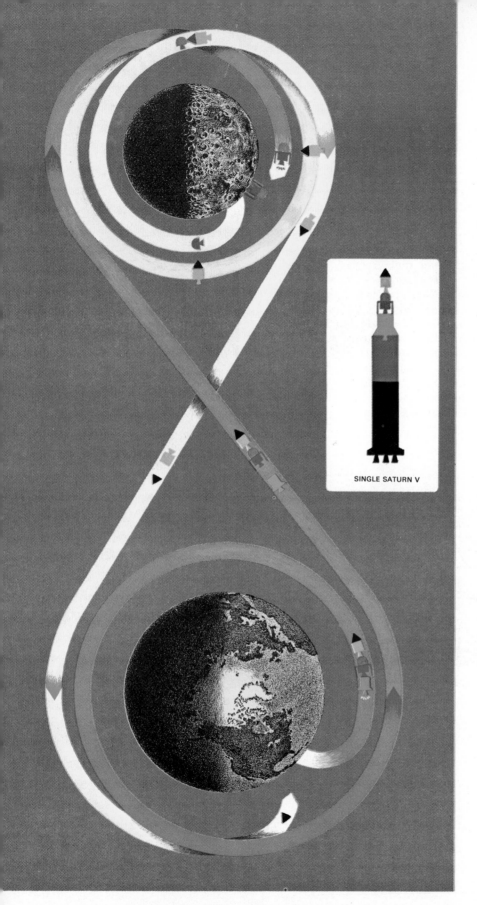

SINGLE SATURN V

LUNAR ORBIT RENDEZVOUS
The approach finally adopted calls for a single Saturn V to boost the Apollo craft, including the Lunar Excursion Module *(purple)*, into an orbit around the moon. Two men in the LEM will descend to the moon and later rendezvous with the main craft before returning to earth.

First Question: How to Go?

Project Apollo confronted planners with three alternatives for getting to the moon. The first—called Direct Flight—specified one huge booster rocket that would push the heavy Apollo spacecraft and its own lunar landing rockets all the way from the earth to the moon. The second—Earth Orbit Rendezvous (EOR)—called for two smaller rockets, which would join forces in an orbit around the earth before proceeding onward. The rocketry would be simpler, but the maneuvers would be far more complicated and chancy. The third —Lunar Orbit Rendezvous (LOR)—involved one Saturn V booster. After going into orbit around the moon, explorers would then descend in a lesser vehicle, like sailors going ashore in a small boat.

In 1961 a tentative decision was made favoring EOR. Almost immediately engineers at NASA's Langley, Virginia, laboratories began pushing for the LOR plan, arguing that it was quicker and cheaper than the others. Some experts opposed LOR; it was a more limited plan, which meant there would be no room for a scientist on the first lunar landings, and it was feared that if, for some reason, a vehicle got into trouble in lunar orbit, it might be beyond help. Computers across the country weighed the pros and cons for months, while the designers waited impatiently. Finally, LOR was ruled best, but the opposition did not die down for months.

The Critical Flight out of Orbit

When the first U.S. lunar visitors have slowed their Apollo spacecraft so that it falls into an orbit girdling the moon, two of the crewmen will crawl into the landing vehicle they have carried with them, seal the hatches and detach it to make the lunar touchdown. This vehicle will have its own rockets to let it land and take off again.

On earth, men are now learning how to lower vehicles to safe landings atop the belching exhausts of rockets. Since the moon has no atmosphere to buoy up wings or parachutes, this landing technique lies at the heart of Project Apollo. It is a crude and costly procedure, for a rocket burns great quantities of fuel—which must be boosted to the moon at the expense of still more fuel. Because of this chain of consumption, it will cost thousands to land every single pound on the moon and lift it off again. The landing must be made quickly, before the LEM burns up its fuel—but it must be made precisely, for there may be no second chance. Unlike an airplane pilot, the LEM pilot who errs in speed and altitude might not have the fuel to come in for a new try.

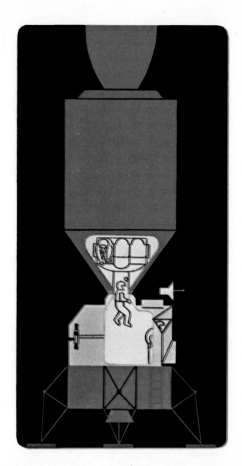

The LEM separates from the Apollo spacecraft, then uses its rockets to brake speed, making a half-turn before landing. To return to orbit

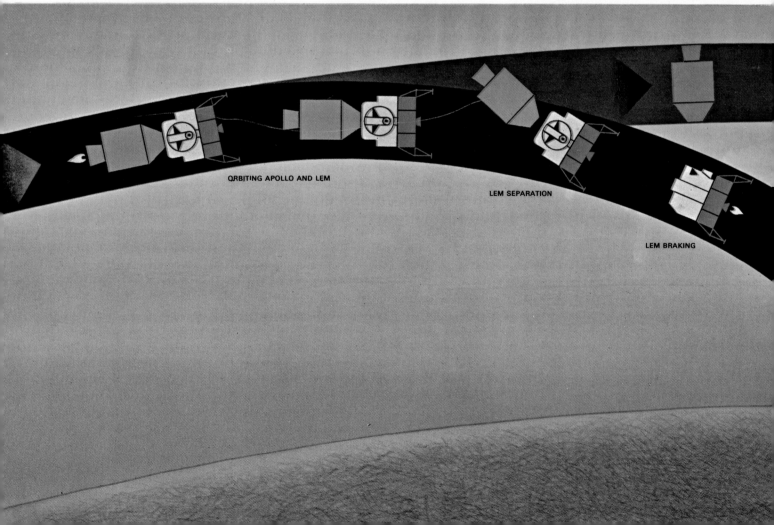

ORBITING APOLLO AND LEM

LEM SEPARATION

LEM BRAKING

READY TO GO ASHORE

Soon after they depart from the earth, the Apollo crewmen detach the Lunar Excursion Module (LEM) from its place in the Saturn V rocket and connect it to the tip of the Apollo manned module. After entering lunar orbit, two of the men will enter the small vehicle and separate from the mother craft for landing. The single crewman left circling in the mother ship can observe his companions' descent and landing—and he can return to earth alone in case of disaster.

CIRCLING FOR A LANDING

The diagram at right shows the path of the Apollo and LEM spacecraft in the vicinity of the moon. The most critical events in the Apollo mission will be those shown here: the descent to a lunar landing and the return to a rendezvous after lunar exploration. These will be accomplished through a close partnership between the human pilots and spaceborne computers, for the maneuvers are too complex and too demanding of precision to be handled by man alone.

DESCENT   ASCENT

it uses its own bottom section as a launching platform, leaving it on the moon. After its rendezvous with Apollo, the LEM is abandoned.

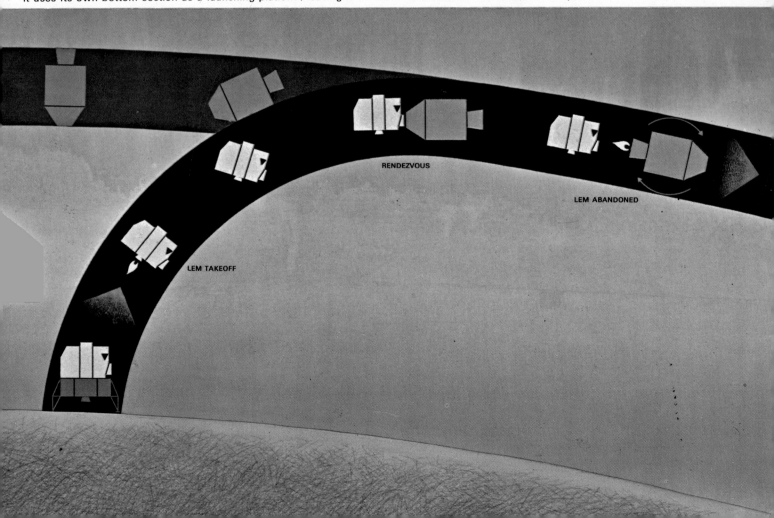

RENDEZVOUS

LEM ABANDONED

LEM TAKEOFF

Final Shape
for a Mighty Booster

U.S. astronauts aiming for the moon will be boosted off earth by the 7.5-million pounds of thrust generated in the Saturn V's cluster of five F-1 rocket engines. Prior to constructing this giant power plant, NASA built what is perhaps the world's biggest mockup—a full-scale model 33 feet in diameter and 138 feet long. At times the mockup held 77 miles of wiring and 5,100 pounds of valves—all for test purposes, to help determine where to put everything in the final production model. The finished booster with its five engines will weigh nearly 175 tons. It will lift the Saturn only 40 miles, but it will put man well on the way to the moon.

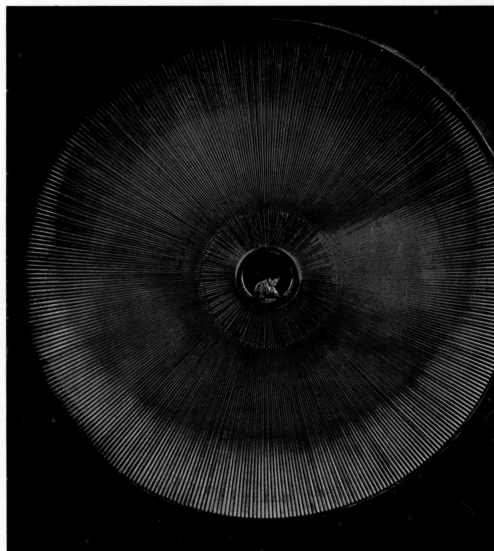

A FULL-SCALE FIRST STAGE
The Saturn V booster mockup, with only one engine attached, looms over workmen in the NASA rocket plant at New Orleans. Around it supervisors in white electric carts with green vacuum bags prowl constantly to maintain almost an operating-room standard of cleanliness.

BIG ENGINE'S BUSINESS END
A rocket specialist adjusts fuel tubes at the center of the funnel-like maw of an F-1 engine. After ignition, fuel at almost 30,000 pounds a second flows from the engine's rim to the firing chamber in the center. This process serves both to cool the engine and preheat the fuel.

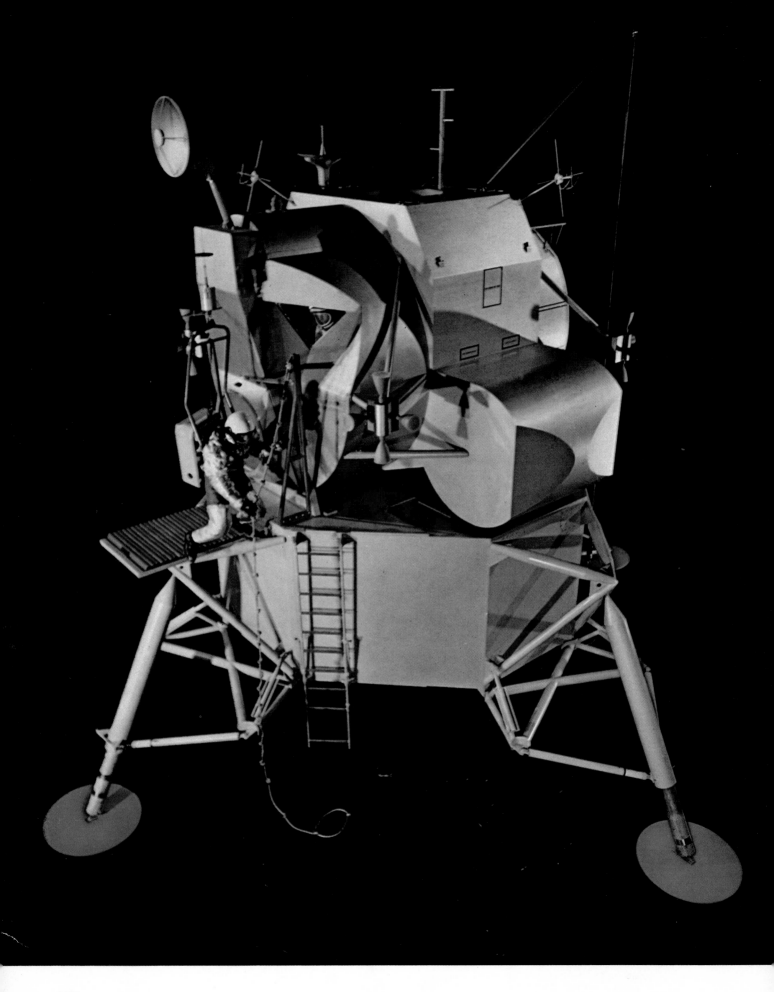

An Ugly but Talented "Bug"

The ungainly LEM, sometimes called "the bug" because of its spraddling legs, is the first manned vehicle designed to function solely in the environment of space. Because it is intended for operation on and around the moon, it needs none of the sleek streamlining required for atmospheric vehicles. This ugly duckling is one of the most complex, ingenious—and hopefully, one of the most reliable—machines ever designed.

Since man knows little about the surface of the moon, the designers had to be sure that the LEM could survive a landing that might be more like a controlled crash, upon a terrain that as far as anyone can tell might consist of deep fissures, breakable crust, huge rocks or deep beds of soft dust. Its landing gear is actually designed in such a way that it can be changed at the last minute to cope with new information.

There was another requirement that was equally exacting. When the time comes to leave the moon, there will be no Cape Kennedy facilities to check out and service the ascent rockets. They must be absolutely dependable and ready to fire, however rough the landing that went before.

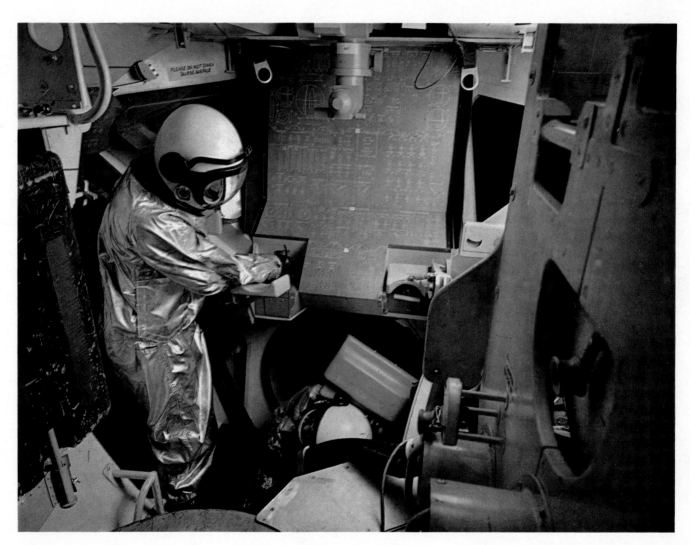

PRACTICING FOR A LUNAR LOWERING
Astronaut Gordon Cooper tries out a knotted rope as a way to lower himself from a wooden mock-up of the LEM at the Grumman Aircraft factory on Long Island. To simulate moon gravity, Cooper is suspended from a counterweighted harness that offsets five sixths of his weight.

TRYING A BUG FOR SIZE
To test whether a fully suited explorer can stir about in the cramped LEM, astronaut Peter Conrad sticks his head into the front hatch visible at the bottom of the picture. Astronaut Gordon Cooper looks on. To save weight, the bug will have no seats. Instead, the pilots will be suspended from the ceiling by parachute-like harnesses during the landing and takeoff.

Travelers Suited for Space

When it comes to lunar exploration, man has certain advantages over machines: he is agile and versatile, and he performs well under unexpected circumstances. But he has disadvantages that help make the Apollo project a formidable task.

Man must be protected in a lunar vacuum that could cause the body's fluids to "boil," that permits temperatures to range over 500 degrees, and that permits lethal blasts of solar radiation and meteorites to spray the lunar surface. To perform exploration under such conditions, the astronaut will look to the clothes upon his back as an all-protective home away from home.

Over the years many people have tried their hand at spacewear design. Buck Rogers, the comic-strip space voyager, wore the casual attire shown here on alien planets in the '30s. More practically, B. F. Goodrich's 1934 suit for Wiley Post was meant to protect its occupant under near-space conditions while he sought to break an airplane altitude record of 47,352 feet.

The basic attire for the first real moon visitor will probably be a "soft" suit like the Project Apollo suit at right, which has bellowslike joints for flexibility. (Without such joints, an astronaut could barely walk when his suit was pressurized). For long stays on the moon, some experts have suggested a hard protective shell—such as the fanciful egg-shaped enclosure shown on the opposite page, or the "canned-man" concept at lower right.

BACK TO THE EGG
One suggested solution to the lunar dangers indicated here is a rigid, egg-shaped shield. Although the one at left is hypothetical, the complex and many-layered Apollo suit beneath it is not. Its layers include a water-cooled inner suit, a main pressure shell and an insulating coverall.

TRENDS IN SPACE FASHIONS
Buck Rogers needed little protection on his comic-strip planets, but Wiley Post's 1934 suit anticipated real space conditions. The Mercury pressure suit was mainly for cooling since the capsule was pressurized. The projected moon suit is intended for wear over several weeks.

BUCK ROGERS UNIFORM

WILEY POST PRESSURE SUIT

PROJECT APOLLO PRESSURE SUIT

PROPOSED MOON SUIT

Manned Mobiles for Rough Terrain

The first moon explorers will make only a few scientific measurements, take some photographs and collect a precious few geological samples before starting back to earth. In their activities they will be limited by the four-hour supplies of oxygen in their space suits to an area of a few hundred yards surrounding their LEM. But for the more extended visits that lie further ahead, there is need for a vehicle to cover much greater distances (the lunar surface is almost as large as the North and South American continents together), to furnish protection and for transporting quantities of life-sustaining but cumbersome supplies.

Any lunar vehicle is likely to be an extraordinary machine. Conventional lubrication will not work, for oil will evaporate in the prevailing vac-

ROLLING ACROSS THE MOON
One proposed solution to the lunar transportation problem is this electrically powered vehicle, which travels on flexible metal wheels. Fitted with a powerful grappling arm, the machine would be able to carry out scientific investigations over a radius of several hundred miles.

uum. Rubber tires would crack or fry in the temperature extremes. Most important, the machines must be able to negotiate unimaginably difficult terrain. Engineers have developed a strange menagerie of experimental lunar vehicles. Some have jointed legs, like insects, for rough ground. Others move on screwlike worms, able to twist through deep dust. Still others roll over dust inside giant balloons.

143

Camping in the Lunar Vacuum

Early Apollo explorers will touch down on the moon for only about 24 hours. For later trips designers may be able to dispense with unnecessary safety equipment, thus permitting supplies to be added for stays of up to two weeks.

The cost of setting up more permanent bases will be tremendous. To sustain six men on a lunar outpost for 90 days *(right)* would require landing some 120,000 pounds of equipment, plus an additional 50,000 pounds every month at a cost of thousands of dollars a pound. The earliest and firmest plan beyond the original Apollo flights is called the Apollo Logistic Support System (ALSS). It will utilize two vehicles (the LEM and a "LEM truck") that can carry shelter and provisions sufficient to last two men for 14 days. Following that, NASA planners envision a Lunar Exploration System for Apollo (LESA), involving a larger "truck" that would permit three men to stay for 90 days. Using modified LESAs as at right, the number of men could be increased to six. Ultimately, as many as 18 men could remain for as long as 24 months.

AT HOME ON THE MOON
An advance scientific base using specialized LESA modules might resemble this scene. In the foreground is a shelter LESA with bunks and showers on the top floor, supplies and generators below. At left, a lunar rover emerges from yet another module, while a communication station LESA stands at rear. A descending LEM brings new personnel to the lunar station.

7

A Ticket
to Neighboring
Worlds

ABOUT THE TIME THE FIRST MEN LAND ON THE MOON, a curious series of events will take place upon the planet Mars. High in its cloudless, indigo sky, a strange, metallic spider will drift slowly groundward. In all the heavens of that distant world, it may be the only moving thing. Presently it will rest upon alien soil, erect its antennae, and speak to the men who launched it half a year before and a hundred million miles away.

That Mars Soft-Lander will carry many instruments capable of performing a wide variety of scientific tests and measurements. Among this array of incredibly specialized devices might be a relatively mundane piece of equipment: an ordinary microphone. In the early stages of man's Martian explorations, the transmission of pictures may be impractical across such a gulf of space. But even from the beginning we should be able to listen.

Those first sounds of another world will be as awe-inspiring, as mind-stretching, as the birth cries of Sputnik I when they beeped from all the world's radios in October 1957. What will we hear? Perhaps the sound of wind sighing across desolate plains, though surely not the boom of waves upon any Martian beach. We may hear the whisper of sliding sand, but we will not hear the patter of falling rain. For on Mars there are no seas, and it never rains.

But we shall hear something, because no world with an atmosphere can be wholly silent. Most exciting of all is the possibility—even though extremely remote—that sooner or later there will be a sound that grows louder and louder, closer and closer. With what eagerness the whole human race would listen if it became clear beyond doubt that some living entity was approaching the fallen space probe. What speculations would ensue if, presently, there came clangings and bumpings and rattlings, all ending suddenly in a grinding crunch and the abrupt cessation of the radio signal.

At the moment, this is fantasy, but it could become reality. As Mariner II demonstrated when it swept past Venus in 1962, the planets are already within reach of automatic probes. In another generation at the

A "SUNFLOWER" FOR SPACE POWER
Missile technicians adjust one gleaming petal of the 30-foot-wide solar power plant called Sunflower. The petals are folded during Sunflower's trip into space. There they blossom out in order to concentrate the heat of the sun to boil mercury. The resulting vapor drives a turbogenerator, providing 3,000 watts of electric power to operate equipment during extended space missions.

most, man will be preparing to follow the trails of his electronic scouts. But today we are as ignorant of the planets as the 15th Century geographers were of Africa or America, and we can be sure that these unexplored lands in space will contain bigger surprises than Victoria Falls or the Grand Canyon.

Although the planets vary in their characteristics even more than do the countries of this earth, they fall into two distinct classes, except for the maverick Pluto. Nearest to the sun are Mercury, Venus, Earth and Mars. They are all fairly small; they are solid bodies and they all have stable surfaces. Venus is nearly the same size as our world, while Mercury and Mars each have about half Earth's diameter.

A grouping of giants

Beyond Mars, there is a sudden change in the scale of the solar system. One might almost imagine that there are two distinct solar systems sharing the same sun. From that inner family of small planets, clustered in a compact group around the sun, there is an abrupt switch to a family of giants scattered over an enormous volume of space. Moreover, all the inner planets are at least as dense as ordinary rock, but the densities of the outer giants are extremely low—approximately that of water. Another odd fact about these huge worlds is their remarkable number of satellites. The four earth-type planets have only three moons among them, but the four outer ones have 28.

It has taken a long time to divest ourselves of the belief that the other planets are no more than slightly exotic earths, doubtless with their own peculiar flora and fauna. A century ago, some astronomers believed that all the planets could have inhabitants. But then, in the face of increasing knowledge, they reluctantly narrowed the list down to Mars and Venus. These closest neighbors of the earth receive about the same amount of solar radiation as does our world. In addition, Mars and Venus definitely possess atmospheres, and this was enough to convince the optimists that they must also possess advanced forms of life. The idea that their atmospheres might be utterly unbreathable was an affront to common sense.

But the universe seems to delight in affronting common sense. By the 1930s astronomers had proved beyond doubt not only that the Martian atmosphere was extremely thin, but also that it contained scarcely a trace of oxygen. This at once ruled out all known forms of animal life—as well as a whole category of science fiction. Not only are there no Martian princesses; there cannot be even a Martian mouse.

But the existence of plants on Mars is still considered possible. Portions of the planet are the characteristic Martian red color throughout the year, and these areas are generally thought to be deserts. There

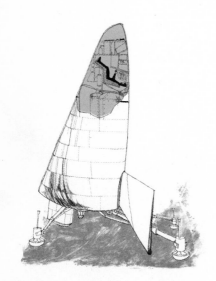

EXCURSION TO MARS
This bullet-shaped spacecraft, shown landing on its tail, is a type proposed as a means of delivering a scientific expedition to the planet Mars. Actually a space shuttle, it would be launched from a larger craft orbiting Mars, and its three-man crew would gather samples of Martian materials and store them inside the detachable "command section" *(blue area).* After a fortnight of exploration, the crew would return to the mother ship in the command unit, leaving behind the vehicle's lower section.

are other regions, located around the warmer central belt of the planet, where regular seasonal changes in color have been observed. These are often assumed to be vegetation whose color varies with the season, in a manner not unlike the seasonal foliage changes on earth. The theory of plant life on Mars gained some support when studies revealed the presence of organic material of the sort associated with vegetation.

It may be that in the remote past Mars did possess a plentiful supply of oxygen; perhaps it is still there. Some experts believe that the red deserts on Mars may be vast stretches of iron oxide, that is, a very pure form of rust. For iron to rust, oxygen must be present. Mars may be a world that literally rusted to death. Long before the first life on earth emerged from the sea, Mars may have supported civilizations of a very high order. Today, we can only speculate about these matters; tomorrow we shall know. At the very least, Mars will keep armies of geologists, astronomers and meteorologists busy for centuries. There is a chance that it will transform biology, giving us our first introduction to extraterrestrial life. But if we are really lucky it will be the archeologists and the historians who will be clamoring for space on the outward-bound ships.

It is impossible to overemphasize the importance of Mars in the future exploration of the solar system. Not only is it the one planet on which we are reasonably confident of finding some form of life, it is the only one which we can explore without first overcoming almost unbelievable technical difficulties.

Mighty like the moon

In contrast, the examination of the two inner planets, Mercury and Venus, would best be conducted at a safe distance from orbiting spaceships. Mercury is a planet which never knows that most fundamental of earthly phenomena, the alternating of day and night. As the moon keeps the same face turned always toward the earth, so Mercury keeps one side perpetually sunward. The temperatures at the center of the bright side may approach 1,000°F.—yet the eternally dark side, never warmed by the rays of the sun, remains at 300° or 400° below zero.

We know almost nothing about the geography of Mercury; the planet is never very far from the glare of the sun, and when it is closest to earth its dark face is turned toward us. A few smudgy maps have been drawn by astronomers, but the details are so vague that they can be of little value. Before long, as techniques of radar examination improve, we may expect more information.

As for Venus, until a few years ago there was still some hope that this planet might be able to harbor forms of life similar to those on earth. The dazzling veil of clouds suggested the presence of vast quantities of water. From this it was only a quick jump in imagination to a steaming world of tropical swamps. This exotic picture has been slow to fade, but it was finally obliterated when Mariner II passed close by Venus and, in 35 minutes of scanning time, eliminated centuries of hopeful speculation.

We now know that the surface of Venus, like that of bright-side Mercury, is unendurably hot; its average temperature is around 800°F. To make the planet still less attractive, the cloud cover and the dense atmosphere make it likely that the surface of Venus is in total darkness. Furthermore, the weight of this atmosphere must be so enormous that to encounter comparable pressures here on earth we would have to go down a half mile into the sea.

Typical of the tenacity with which Venus holds its secrets is the fact that, after more than three centuries of telescopic observation, we do not know Venus' period of rotation. Recent radar measurements make it fairly certain that the planet turns very slowly on its axis. Like Mercury, Venus may keep one face turned always toward the sun. It might be reasonable therefore to expect the other side of the planet to be extremely cold—but it is not. On the contrary, it is almost as hot as the side that faces the sun. The thick blanket of atmosphere is believed to act as a heat-equalizer; tremendous gales, of a ferocity we cannot even imagine, may accompany this atmospheric heat exchange.

The winter of the giants

Considering such obstacles, the exploration of Venus will demand not only technical skill but also vast courage. And amid all of the mysteries veiled by the clouds of Venus, one thing is certain: the chances of finding life there are virtually nil.

Beyond the zone of the terrestrial planets, out past Mars, the light and heat of the sun fade slowly into a deepening twilight—an eternal winter that will never know a spring. In this winter the giant planets Jupiter, Saturn, Uranus and Neptune move ponderously along their orbits, the outermost taking more than a century and a half to complete one revolution around the sun.

Before we reach the giants, however, there is a mysterious no-man's-land, more than 300 million miles wide, which appears littered with the debris of some primeval catastrophe. Between Mars and Jupiter circulate thousands of minor planets, or asteroids, most of them irregularly shaped rocks only a few miles across. Some have orbits that wander sunward, so that occasionally they pass close to earth or even collide with it. Arizona's famous Meteor Crater may be the site of an encounter with a very small asteroid. One theoretical explanation of the asteroids is that they are the fragmentary remains of a former planet destroyed during the early history of the solar system.

In our space-faring future, the asteroids may be of importance only as

MARINER II,
DECEMBER 14, 1962

VENUS

SUN

EARTH,
MARINER II
LAUNCHED
AUGUST 27, 1962

MARVEL OF REMOTE CONTROL

The amazing voyage of Mariner II (its route is shown in blue) proved that a spacecraft can be tracked and guided across vast distances. For more than 100 days and 180 million miles, Mariner II maintained constant communication with the earth and obeyed all commands sent to it. In accordance with plans, the satellite was guided to within 22,000 miles of Venus—so close that its path was radically altered by Venus' gravity.

a slight menace to navigation. On the other hand, they may be of great scientific value. Quite recently, and very unexpectedly, the asteroids have become involved in the debates about the presence of life in outer space. Some investigators have found that certain meteorites—believed to have originated in the asteroid belt—contain very complex carbon compounds of the kind associated with living creatures. This certainly does not prove that there is life among the asteroids. But the great surprise is to discover organic materials at all in an environment so fiercely hostile as the asteroid belt.

A meteorological mystery

By a strange reversal of scientific opinion, the giant planet Jupiter now appears to have a better chance of supporting life than the recent favorite, Venus. As in the case of Venus, however, what we see when we look at Jupiter is its cloud cover; for Jupiter has an immensely deep atmosphere, composed of free hydrogen and ammonia, along with methane and other carbon compounds. This covering of clouds is in a very turbulent state. Even a small telescope shows that vast meteorological disturbances are taking place. The planet is girdled by parallel belts of clouds, like those caused by the trade winds of earth but on a tenfold greater scale.

Although Jupiter's cloud cover is constant, most of the cloud markings we see there are quite transient, and disappear after a few days or weeks. However, there is one puzzling formation which has remained visible, on and off, for at least 130 years. This is the famous Great Red Spot, an oval-shaped mass lying parallel to the planet's equator and not far from it, in the Southern Hemisphere. The Great Red Spot is considerably larger than our entire earth, yet it drifts around Jupiter like a gigantic raft; it has made several revolutions of the planet during the century that it has been under intense observation. The most popular theory holds that the Great Red Spot is a huge meteorological disturbance.

While the outermost reaches of Jupiter's atmosphere are extremely cold, the internal temperature is probably quite high, due to a "greenhouse effect," in which the atmosphere acts as an insulator to hold in heat from the sun. Water might exist there, permitting the formation of the "organic soup" which sparked the first earthly seeds of life. It is now believed, in fact, that Jupiter's hydrogen-ammonia-methane type of atmosphere is what existed on the primitive earth in the days when life made its first appearance.

The investigation of Jupiter, whether by robot probes or manned vehicles, will be an undertaking even more difficult than that posed by Venus. Apart from any other consideration, a surface gravity two and a half times that of the earth's would make it an uncomfortable place for human beings. The explorers would need self-powered prosthetic devices

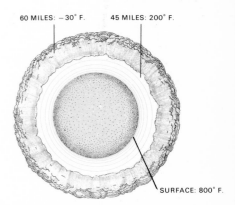

VENUS OBSERVED

Little is known about the surface of Venus, shrouded as it is by clouds, except that it is hot—800° F., according to temperature studies made by Mariner II—hot enough to melt lead and hot enough to preclude life as we know it on earth. This infernal heat is maintained by the 50-mile-high, 15-mile-thick cloud layer, which acts as a thermal blanket.

simply to move their arms and legs, and would be glad to relax in baths during their off-duty hours. Moreover, the pressure in the atmosphere of Jupiter is so great that any spaceship entering it would have to be designed like a bathyscaphe. Such a spaceship would also require fantastic power to overcome Jupiter's surface gravity for the return voyage to earth.

Jupiter and its 12 satellites constitute a miniature solar system in themselves. They are worlds in their own right; the largest, Ganymede, is as large as the planet Mercury. It will take decades to explore all these strange and lonely worlds; no one can predict what may be found on them, or in what way they may serve man in the centuries to come.

The symmetry of Saturn

Beyond Jupiter, in the deepening cold, floats that most glorious of all celestial apparitions—Saturn, with its incredible system of rings. No one can ever forget his first glimpse of this wonderful sight, visible through even a small telescope. It seems as if a tiny, exquisite model is floating there in space; the rings appear too complicated and too symmetrical to be the work of nature. To the first observers they seemed to be solid, but today we know that they are composed of countless particles of dust and ice, each itself a tiny satellite moving in an independent orbit around the mother planet. It is as if an eternal hailstorm is sweeping forever around Saturn.

The planet itself is very similar to Jupiter, though not quite so large or so prone to atmospheric disturbances. It has at least nine moons— and one of them, Titan, is the largest of all satellites in the solar system, and the only moon which possesses an atmosphere (methane with traces of ammonia).

We know practically nothing about Uranus and Neptune, except that they are smaller and colder relatives of Jupiter and Saturn. All four planets have deep, hydrogen-rich atmospheres, and despite their great size they all spin very rapidly on their axes. Jupiter, though it is 11 times the diameter of earth, has a day of less than 10 hours. Even Neptune, with the longest rotation period of the four, has a day only about half as long as the earth's.

The presently known limits of the solar system are reached at Pluto, which breaks all the rules and is now something of an astronomical scandal. For some years, astronomers had noticed that the outermost planets, Uranus and Neptune, were not moving in exact accordance with the laws of gravitation. Instead, their paths showed slight irregularities which could best be explained by the attraction of an unknown body still farther from the sun.

Analyzing these irregularities, the American astronomer Percival Lowell calculated the position of a hypothetical planet, and after a long search Pluto was located in 1930 by astronomers at the Lowell Observatory in Flagstaff, Arizona. The achievement was hailed as a great triumph for mathematics—but now, astonishingly, it seems that Pluto is too small to account for the effects which led to its discovery. It must have been discovered by sheer luck coupled with hard work.

Of all the planets, we know the least about Pluto. In fact we know for certain only its distance from the earth and the length of its day, six times longer than ours. It has an unusually elliptical orbit which cuts across the orbit of the next planet, Neptune; as a result, for a few decades after 1969, Neptune, and not Pluto, will be the most distant planet from the sun.

To complete the roll call of the solar system one must mention the comets, of which unknown millions travel around the sun, many of them in orbits stretching halfway to the nearer stars. Though they are the most spectacular of all heavenly bodies, dominating the night sky for weeks on end during their rare appearances, they are actually only tenuous wisps of gas containing little solid matter. A spaceship could no more land on a comet than an airplane can land on a cloud, but before long scientists will send a space probe into the heart of a passing comet and collect samples of the rocks and frozen gases that may be churning around in its nucleus.

Settlers in space

Today, no one can predict the rate at which we shall spread out across the solar system, or the extent to which we shall be able to exploit it. Nuclear propulsion, which is bound to come, will make all the planets easily accessible. A century from now, Pluto will seem closer to our grandchildren than the earth's poles did to our grandparents.

And by that time, we will almost certainly have established bases on the more important bodies in the solar system. Many will be automated with equipment that requires servicing and refueling only at long intervals. But others will be permanently staffed and in time may grow into something more than scientific bases. They may eventually become self-sustaining colonies—even independent societies.

Let there be no doubt: the powers that are now coming into our hands will be sufficient to reshape the solar system, as we have already reshaped the earth. Even before the modern era Western man had lived for 1,000 years in a partly artificial environment. He had transformed entire countries into those biochemical processing plants called "farms," which are quite as unnatural as any automated production line. This was done by the labor of his own hands, with no power sources but wind and water, horses and oxen. Yet today he may press a button and destroy a mountain or create a sea. With such powers, the large-scale mod-

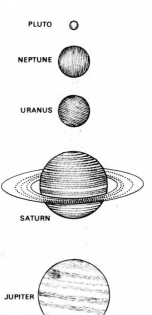

PLUTO

NEPTUNE

URANUS

SATURN

JUPITER

MARS

EARTH

VENUS

MERCURY

SUN

CONTRASTS IN COMPOSITION

Space travelers may find striking distinctions in the compositions of the planets. The four close to the sun are hard-surfaced. But Jupiter, Saturn, Uranus and Neptune may have no "surface" at all. These "gas giants" may consist simply of ammonia, hydrogen, etc., which take the form of gas in the outer atmosphere, gradually thickening to a liquid and then to a solid state toward the core. Mysterious Pluto has yet to be classified.

ification of entire planetary environments need be only a matter of time.

However, subtlety is sometimes more efficient than power. Professor Carl Sagan has pointed out that we might prepare Venus for human habitation by "microbiological engineering." The upper atmosphere of Venus might be seeded with a variety of algae which would break down the immense quantities of carbon dioxide present there, and release free oxygen. As the atmosphere was slowly processed—an operation which might take centuries, but which would be automatic once started—the temperature would gradually fall, since the greenhouse effect that now traps heat on the planet would become less efficient. And so, at a date closer to us than Columbus' immortal voyage, Venus might become a new home for man.

There will be many such homes as the centuries lengthen into millennia. And as our aggressive young species spreads across the solar system, perhaps it is just as well that there is so little likelihood of meeting any other form of intelligence. We would probably exploit or exterminate technically inferior races, and superior races might treat us with justice rather than mercy. It may be that in the exploration of a vast and largely hostile planetary system we shall complete our racial adolescence, learning the skills and wisdom that will be needed when we finally make contact with other intelligences.

Blazing Trails through the Solar System

Not long after man has touched down on the moon, he will head out into the exotic and mysterious reaches of the solar system (opposite). The problems will be staggering. Flights of this kind with conventional rockets would cost billions of dollars. Prolonged weightlessness might pose a threat to health. On extended journeys, a rocket's complex electronic mechanism could break down. The vehicles might have to run a gauntlet of deadly solar storms and meteoroids. To surmount such difficulties, radical new nuclear-powered rockets are planned. They would have ingenious "meteor bumpers"; they might spin in flight to produce artificial gravity; perhaps they will use magnetic fields, or their own hydrogen propellant, as shielding against solar flares. But the ultimate problem will be human. Tomorrow's astronaut will have to be a jack-of-all-space-age-trades —astronavigator, computer repairman, doctor and dentist, even archeologist.

AN ABSTRACT OF OUTER SPACE
This painting is an abstraction conveying some of the eerie, other-worldly quality of man's future flight through space. The white swirls symbolize the trajectories and orbits of rockets speeding through the solar system; the pink spheres stand for the planets. Yuri Vasiliev, the youthful Soviet artist who painted it, says that he got his inspiration from "nuclear physics and the space age."

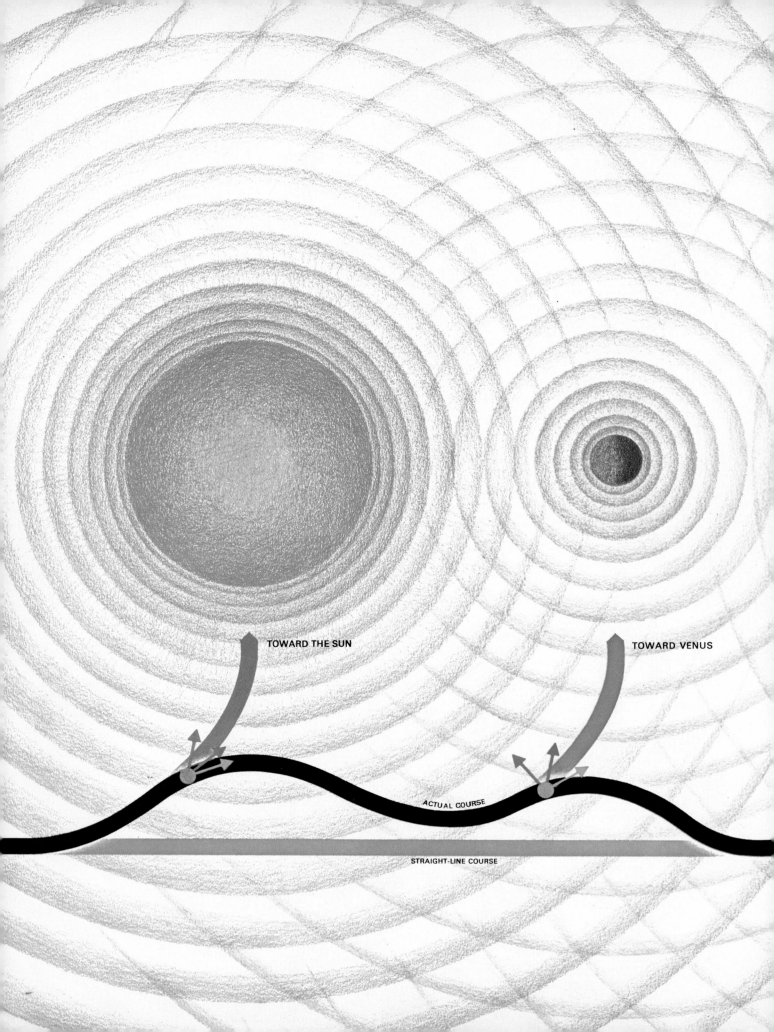

TOWARD THE SUN

TOWARD VENUS

ACTUAL COURSE

STRAIGHT-LINE COURSE

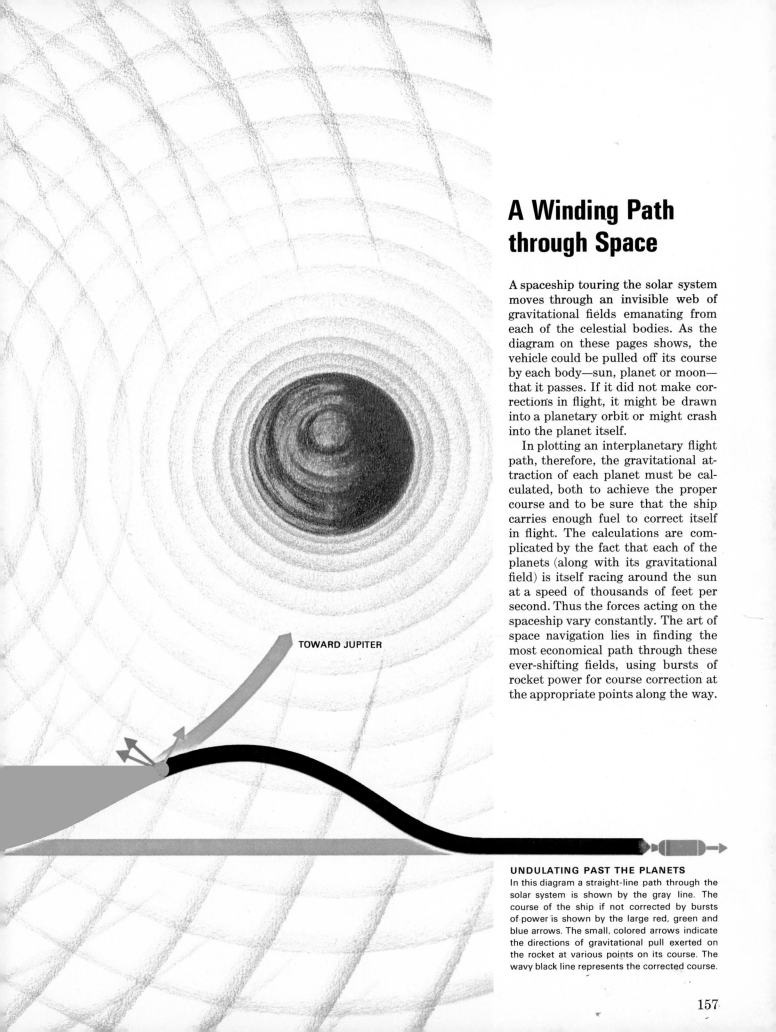

A Winding Path through Space

A spaceship touring the solar system moves through an invisible web of gravitational fields emanating from each of the celestial bodies. As the diagram on these pages shows, the vehicle could be pulled off its course by each body—sun, planet or moon—that it passes. If it did not make corrections in flight, it might be drawn into a planetary orbit or might crash into the planet itself.

In plotting an interplanetary flight path, therefore, the gravitational attraction of each planet must be calculated, both to achieve the proper course and to be sure that the ship carries enough fuel to correct itself in flight. The calculations are complicated by the fact that each of the planets (along with its gravitational field) is itself racing around the sun at a speed of thousands of feet per second. Thus the forces acting on the spaceship vary constantly. The art of space navigation lies in finding the most economical path through these ever-shifting fields, using bursts of rocket power for course correction at the appropriate points along the way.

TOWARD JUPITER

UNDULATING PAST THE PLANETS
In this diagram a straight-line path through the solar system is shown by the gray line. The course of the ship if not corrected by bursts of power is shown by the large red, green and blue arrows. The small, colored arrows indicate the directions of gravitational pull exerted on the rocket at various points on its course. The wavy black line represents the corrected course.

Timetable
to Mars

The same liquid-fueled spacecraft that is used to put a man on the moon could take astronauts up for a look at Mars in the early 1970s, after refueling in orbit. NASA has already prepared flight plans to meet a celestial deadline: in 1971 the earth and Mars will be closer than they will be again until 1986.

The first flights will be "flyby" reconnaissance trips, as diagramed on this page. The rocket will be able to use the orbital speed of the earth (about 66,000 miles per hour) for part of its boost by leaving in the same direction that the earth is following around the sun. With an extra thrust to get clear of the earth's gravitational field, the rocket will fall into its own elliptical orbit about the sun: this route will carry it past Mars and then back to earth.

In such a flight, and in later landings on Mars *(opposite page)*, navigators will have to make in-flight course adjustments; even the best-laid flight plans cannot account for errors in launching or for inaccuracies in the predicted paths of planets.

AROUND THE SUN IN 641 DAYS
This diagram represents the flight path of a projected trip past Mars. The congruence of the earth and Mars in the early 1970s would allow a Saturn rocket, even with its limited chemical fuel supply, to hurl itself out of the earth's orbit *(orange)*, cross the path of Mars *(red)* as it coasts in an elliptical orbit about the sun *(purple)*, and ultimately return to earth again.

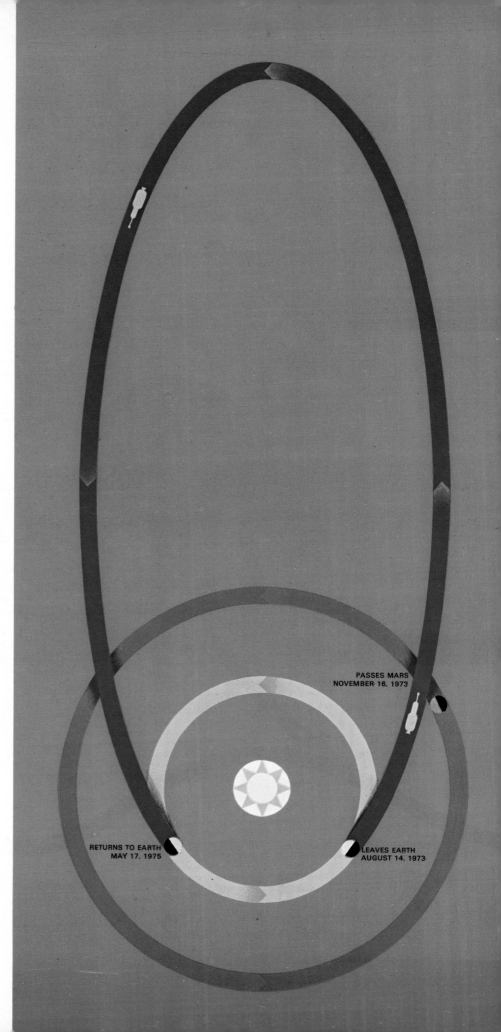

PASSES MARS
NOVEMBER 16, 1973

RETURNS TO EARTH
MAY 17, 1975

LEAVES EARTH
AUGUST 14, 1973

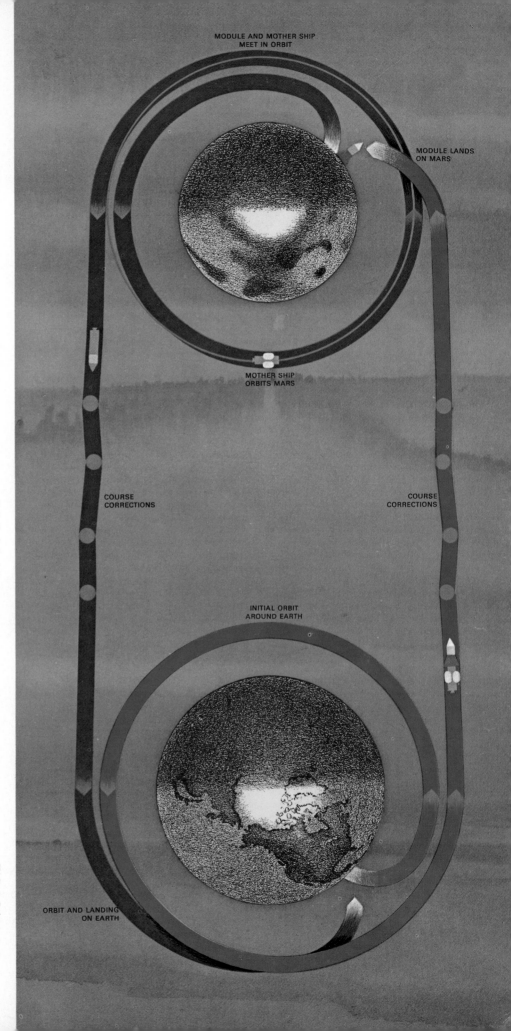

MODULE AND MOTHER SHIP
MEET IN ORBIT

MODULE LANDS
ON MARS

MOTHER SHIP
ORBITS MARS

COURSE
CORRECTIONS

COURSE
CORRECTIONS

INITIAL ORBIT
AROUND EARTH

ORBIT AND LANDING
ON EARTH

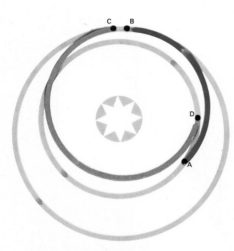

STOPOVER IN SPACE

In a Mars landing mission *(above)*, a rocket traces trajectories about the sun to intersect Mars and the earth in their own solar orbits *(orange)*. The rocket leaves earth (A) April 30, 1971, on a course *(violet)* that gets it to Mars (B) September 16, 1971. After a 10-day stop, the rocket takes off from Mars (C) in a different orbit *(blue)* to meet earth (D) June 2, 1972.

MANEUVERS IN TWO ORBITS

To land on Mars a rocket is first orbited around the earth, where it picks up extra fuel before accelerating to escape the earth's gravitation. Near Mars, the mother ship goes into orbit while a small space module lands. The module later returns to the mother ship, which in turn accelerates to get back to earth. Small course corrections are carried out in flight *(color dots)*.

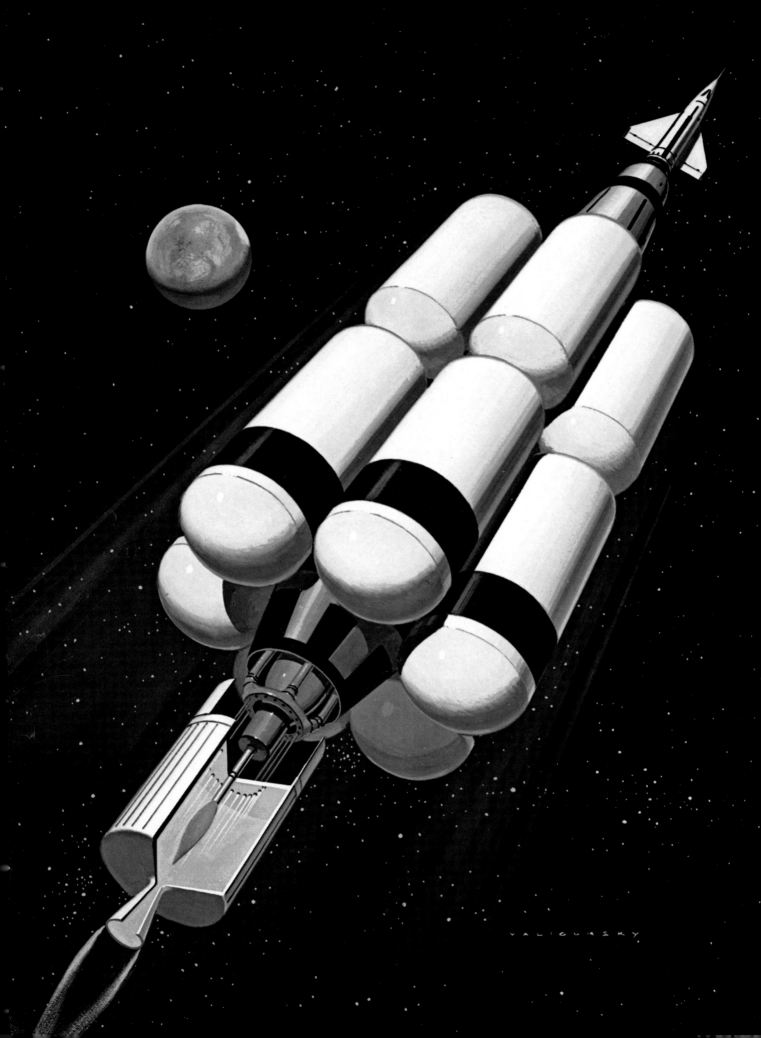

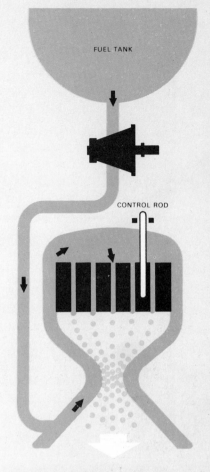

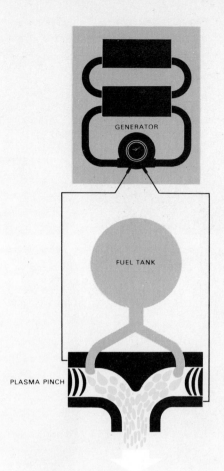

Economy Runs with Nuclear Fuels

Rockets cannot lift enough conventional liquid or solid fuel for much interplanetary maneuvering. For a landing on Mars, or a planet-hopping excursion through the solar system, nuclear-powered rockets must be designed. Experimental plutonium reactors have been tested, and dozens of new nuclear engines are on the drawing boards and in development.

In conventional rockets, the fuel itself is expelled to propel the craft. In nuclear propulsion, the uranium or plutonium fuel may be used in two ways. It can be exploded to serve as a propellant, or it can generate radiation to improve the performance of certain propellants. The radiation may be used to heat the propellant or to generate electricity that pinches it into a thin high-velocity stream; each method increases the propellant's efficiency. Conventional boosters will still have to be used to lift a rocket off the earth. But once aloft, nuclear fuels can furnish the longer-lasting thrust required to keep a vehicle going over the immense distances of space. Advanced designs of such engines may get up to eight times more energy per unit of fuel as present chemically fueled rockets.

A PINCH OF PROPULSION
In this "plasma pinch engine" a nuclear reactor provides the heat to generate electric current. A propellant is fed into a Y-shaped airless chamber, the two closed ends of which are electrodes. The electrodes turn the propellant into plasma, a hot ionized gas, and also create an electromagnetic "pinching," or compression of the plasma in the chamber. This forces it out a rear opening to propel the rocket forward.

SUPERHOT SPRAY
In the standard nuclear engine, cold liquid hydrogen is pumped into a compact atomic reactor, as shown; there the heat of fission raises its temperature thousands of degrees. No lox is needed, resulting in a more efficient propellant. This pure hot hydrogen is spewed out through a nozzle. Cadmium control rods keep the fission in check. The more heat the reactor can contain, the more efficient the engine.

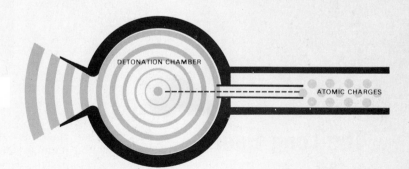

A MIGHTY ATOMIC BOOST
The "gaseous core" reactor, a theoretical innovation that might power a Mars-bound rocket *(opposite)*, would have a gaseous jet of uranium or plutonium contained at the center of an open chamber. Liquid hydrogen stored in tanks around the rocket would be squirted into the reactor chamber and would be heated by the radiation to form a powerful high-speed exhaust.

EXPLOSIVE EXHAUST
One of the most radical nuclear propulsion ideas, diagramed here, involves the explosion of small nuclear charges in a detonation chamber. The force of the explosion pushes against the walls of the chamber, thus impelling the rocket ahead. In other similar designs, charges are set off just behind the spaceship, rather than inside it, pushing against a rear-end bumper plate.

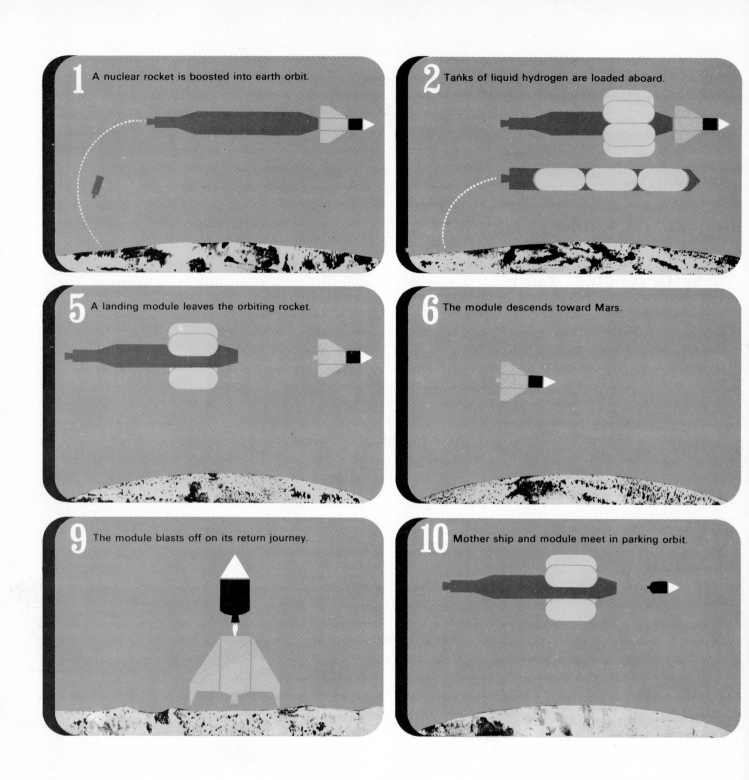

1 A nuclear rocket is boosted into earth orbit.

2 Tanks of liquid hydrogen are loaded aboard.

5 A landing module leaves the orbiting rocket.

6 The module descends toward Mars.

9 The module blasts off on its return journey.

10 Mother ship and module meet in parking orbit.

The Long Haul to Mars

By the time man flies to Mars the skies will be populated by a host of new rocket breeds—space tankers, space ferries, space tugs and enormous nuclear-powered long-haul rockets. All of these vehicles probably will be involved in the Mars mission.

As this flight is foreseen now, it may occur this way: a nuclear rocket about 260 feet long is launched into an earth orbit. There, clip-on fuel tanks, brought up from earth by space tankers, are attached to it with the aid of small, maneuverable space tugs. With a crew of up to seven men, the rocket reaches Mars 180 days after leaving orbit. The vehicle is guided into a parking orbit around the planet, the crew selects a landing site and two men descend in a detachable excursion module. The 350-mile descent takes about one hour. A parachute

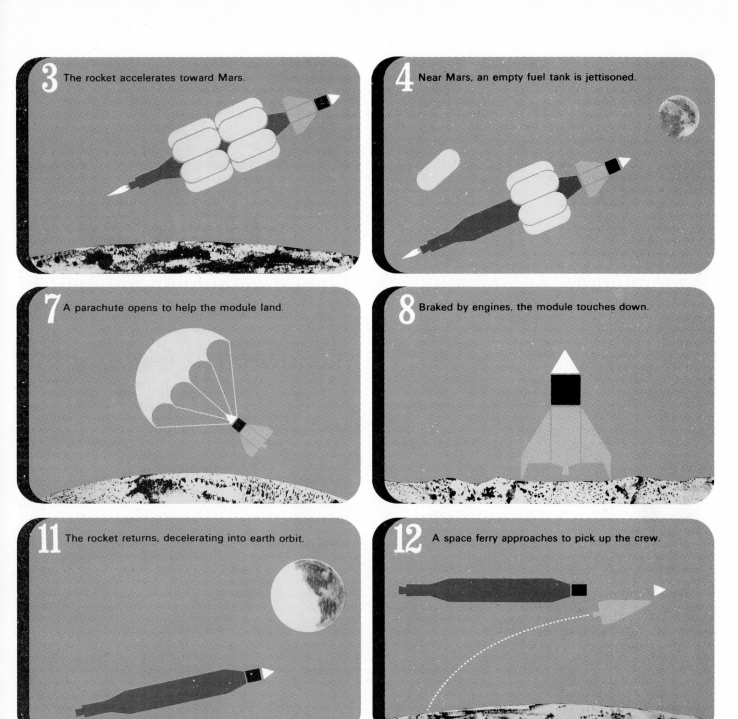

3 The rocket accelerates toward Mars.

4 Near Mars, an empty fuel tank is jettisoned.

7 A parachute opens to help the module land.

8 Braked by engines, the module touches down.

11 The rocket returns, decelerating into earth orbit.

12 A space ferry approaches to pick up the crew.

and small rocket engines ensure that the module lands upright on its own built-in launching pad. After a stay of between 10 and 40 days, the explorers put their module back into the parking orbit and rendezvous with the mother ship for a 200-day trip back to earth. As the rocket enters into an earth orbit, astronauts and instruments are picked up by a space ferry for the return shuttle to the earth.

STOCKED FOR SPACE TRAVEL
A round trip to Mars, shown above in 12 stages, requires an ingenious assortment of hardware and mechanical parts—for example, fuel tanks that are jettisoned when empty, and a detachable launching pad, parachute and takeoff engines. The landing module is stocked with some 2,000 pounds of scientific equipment, including a portable meteorological station and a powerful radio for communication with the earth, as well as a tracked car for exploring the Martian terrain.

163

A Springboard into Space

All excursions into the solar system, whether local hops to the moon or long-distance probes to Pluto, will someday take off from an orbit about the earth. By accelerating in the same direction it is orbiting in, a rocket can use its orbital speed to help boost it into space: a rocket in orbit already has 70 per cent of the speed it needs to go to the moon. What is more, a rocket bound for one of the planets can get a further boost from the earth's own rotation about the sun.

The direction the rocket takes into space depends partly on its rate of acceleration in leaving the earth orbit, as shown in the diagram on these pages.

Somewhat the same principle can be utilized to speed a rocket on its way far out in space. Thus, to cut down on fuel expenditure and travel time to Pluto, a spaceship could be launched first toward Jupiter; passing through Jupiter's gravitational field it would be sent with an added boost toward Pluto. Such a mission would take only about 25 years—almost 22 years less than a flight direct to Pluto. This is the principle of gravity boost or propulsion—using a planet's gravity as a booster.

"Gravity propulsion," explains one farsighted space scientist, "is free energy, available in reliable form for the price of some clever guidance."

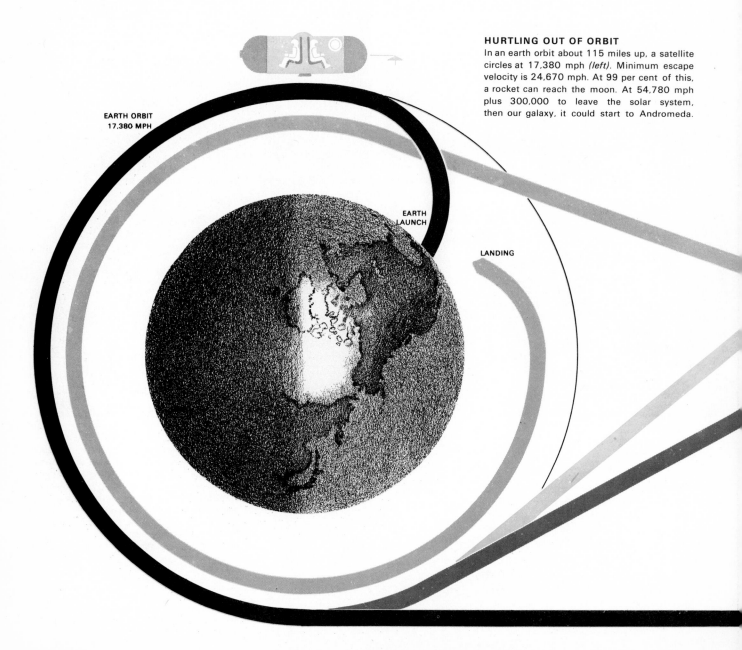

EARTH ORBIT
17,380 MPH

EARTH LAUNCH

LANDING

HURTLING OUT OF ORBIT
In an earth orbit about 115 miles up, a satellite circles at 17,380 mph *(left)*. Minimum escape velocity is 24,670 mph. At 99 per cent of this, a rocket can reach the moon. At 54,780 mph plus 300,000 to leave the solar system, then our galaxy, it could start to Andromeda.

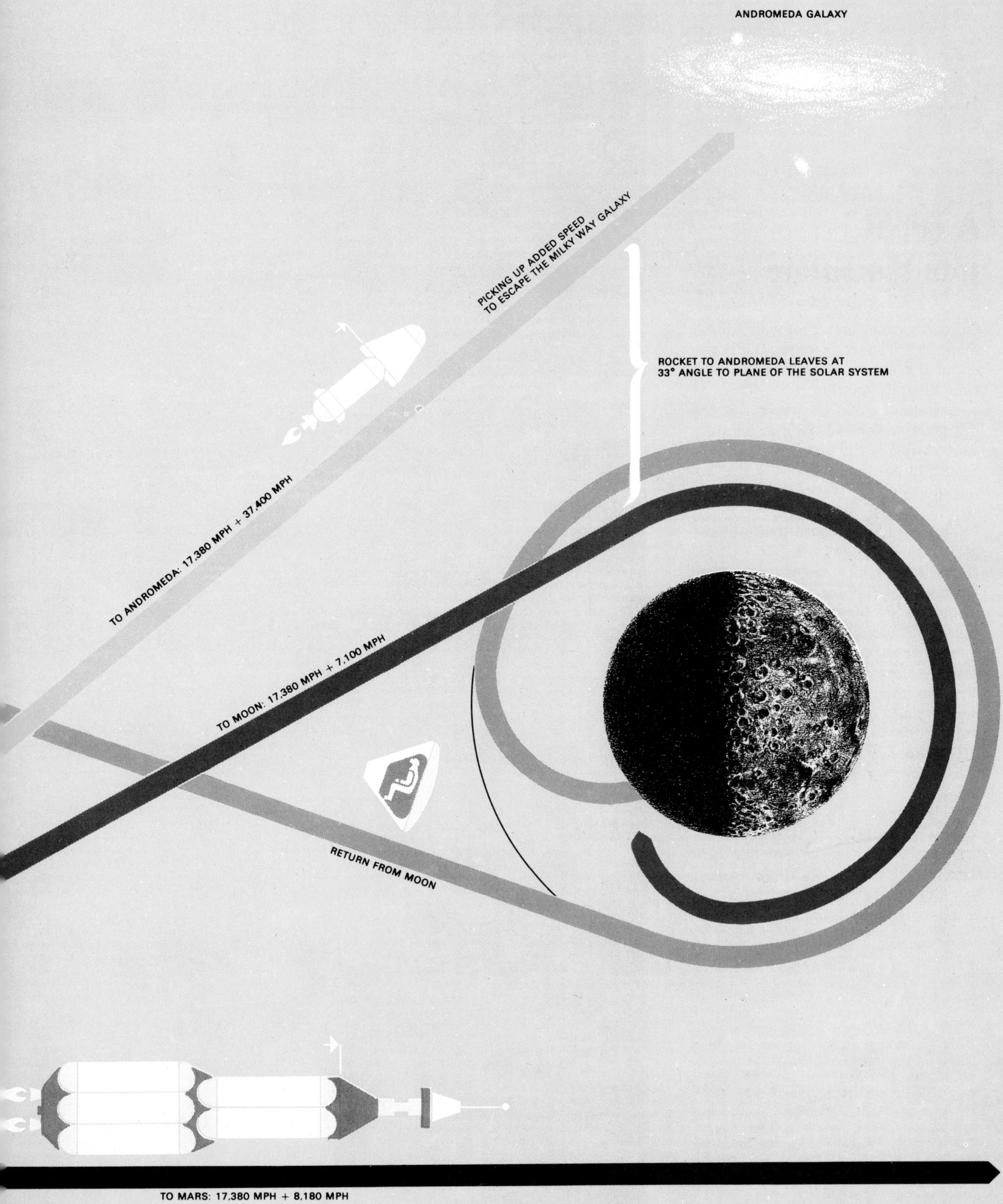

ANDROMEDA GALAXY

PICKING UP ADDED SPEED
TO ESCAPE THE MILKY WAY GALAXY

ROCKET TO ANDROMEDA LEAVES AT
33° ANGLE TO PLANE OF THE SOLAR SYSTEM

TO ANDROMEDA: 17,380 MPH + 37,400 MPH

TO MOON: 17,380 MPH + 7,100 MPH

RETURN FROM MOON

TO MARS: 17,380 MPH + 8,180 MPH

A Flight into the Future

On earth, time and tide wait for no man. But in space, a man traveling at about the speed of light would find time all but standing still. Thus, if an astronaut could be sent to the Andromeda galaxy and back at lightlike speeds *(right)*, the earth would have aged four million years—but the astronaut might be only 56 years older —on his return.

This paradox is more than a flight of fancy. First proposed by Albert Einstein, it is now supported by experimental evidence from the world of atomic particles. Short-lived mesons take much longer to decay when moving at superspeeds than when in relative slow motion: their life-spans are stretched out just as an astronaut's would be if he traveled at millions of miles per hour.

Nonetheless, flight to the distant stars must remain a dream for the foreseeable future. Construction of rockets that even approach the speed of light (670 million miles per hour) is probably centuries off. For our lifetime we will have to settle for space-age flivvers that merely putter along at tens of thousands of miles per hour.

SHOOTING FOR A STAR
The diagram at right shows one possible flight plan for a journey to Andromeda. Though the rocket accelerates at one g for half the trip and decelerates the rest, it attains lightlike speeds in about a year. At midpoint its top speed is 99.99-999999995 per cent of the speed of light.

EARTH ON DEPARTURE

ANDROMEDA GALAXY

TWO MILLION LIGHT-YEARS FROM EARTH

ASTRONAUT AGES 28 YEARS

HE AGES 28 MORE YEARS

EARTH ON RETURN

EARTH AGES FOUR MILLION YEARS

8

Calling across the Great Silence

A NEIGHBORING NEBULA
Through the giant 200-inch lens of the Mount Palomar observatory, one of the bright lights in the Big Dipper is revealed as a spiral nebula—a galaxy, like the Milky Way, containing millions of stars. Most of the older stars in the universe have planets, and scientists now believe that a vast number of these planets may provide conditions that would support life.

there are strange stars near Arcturus
Voices are crying an unknown name in the sky

—ARCHIBALD MACLEISH

Epistle to Be Left in the Earth

IT WAS CENTURIES before mankind realized the true size of the solar system, with its planets circling hundreds—even thousands—of millions of miles apart. Yet, when measured against the far greater immensities of the universe, earth and its sister planets appear as a tight and compact family, huddling close to the warmth of their central sun. Even the most far-ranging of the explorations within our solar system will cover scarcely one ten-thousandth of the distance to the nearest star.

But it is among the stars rather than our sister planets that we must search if we hope to find intelligence. Even if Mars or Venus now harbors life, it would be a fantastic coincidence if that life happened to be anywhere near our own level of development.

We must never forget the immensity of the universe in time as well as distance. Our own solar system is about five billion years old. Within that system, life has existed on the planet earth for perhaps two and a half billion years. Only in the last million years has the toolmaking animal called man become dominant; only in the last 5,000 years has he started asking questions of the stars; and only in the last 50 has he made any real strides toward answering them. Assuming an evolutionary development paralleling our own, the odds become roughly a million to one against our encountering, in this solar system, any sort of beings comparable even to the ancient Babylonian astrologer-priests—much less the satellite builders of the space age.

However, if instead of taking the parochial solar viewpoint we stand off and look at the cosmos, in which every star is itself a sun, these astronomical odds are reversed. It now appears that of these distant suns, perhaps as many as one in 10 has habitable planets orbiting it. In our own galaxy—much of which is invisible even with the largest telescopes —there may be billions of "earths," many of them supporting life.

But how to contact that life, if it is intelligent, or to observe it, if it is not? To visualize the problem of interstellar communication, we must construct some kind of model. Let us do so on the hardly generous scale of one foot to every million miles, which will really cut the solar system down to size.

Mars and Venus are then 35 and 25 feet away; we can almost think of them as the houses next door. We suspect that both are unoccupied; certainly their thermostats are set at most uncomfortable levels.

The other "houses" of our little solar suburb are ranged around us at distances varying from 20 yards to about two thirds of a mile. Now that space travel is possible, we shall soon go visiting, starting with our immediate neighbors and working outward. It may take us a century to make all our calls, but there is no hurry. After all, only five centuries ago we were not aware even of all the rooms in our own house.

An ice-covered door, a vacant lot

In the year 2050, we will be knocking on the ice-covered door marked "Pluto." But beyond Pluto is a vacant lot of considerable size: in our scaled-down solar system, something on the order of 5,000 miles.

There we come to our nearest stellar neighbors, the star system of Alpha Centauri, but it is possible that we shall not find anyone at home. Rather, we will have to range out several times this distance if we expect our search to be successful. If there are any neighbors in residence within 10,000 miles, it will be quite surprising. But—if there are no neighbors within 100,000 miles, it will be incredible.

As recently as the 1930s, astronomers believed the stars were lonely cosmic suns, without any planets of their own. Indeed, the popular astronomy books of that day often asserted that our solar system was probably unique, and that earth might well be the only inhabited planet in the universe. This viewpoint was the last stand of the pre-Copernican geocentric outlook. And though it flourished only a generation ago, today it seems as outmoded as that of the medieval philosophers who believed that the lights in the sky were pinpricks in the mighty heavens.

The idea of earth's uniqueness was not based on mere prejudice. It seemed to the astronomers of the '30s and earlier that planets could be created only by a very rare event—the near collision of two stars, wherein the violent gravitational attraction would rip out sufficient matter from each to form planets. But space is so empty that the coming-together of two stars in this way could happen not more than a few times during the whole history of the universe.

In the 1940s this collision, or "tidal," theory fell into disrepute; it could not account for the facts. Moreover, through bitter experience over centuries, astronomers had grown suspicious of any theory that indicated a special or privileged place for our solar system. Methods had been suggested whereby even isolated suns might give birth to planets without the intervention of another star. Other planetary systems might, therefore, be fairly common; but how common, no one could guess.

Part of the reason for the widespread notion that planets were unique to our solar system was the fact that astronomers had no way to detect anything so small as a planet in outer space. But then, in 1942, a minute deviation was observed in the path of the double star known as 61 Cygni. This deviation could only be explained by the fact that 61 Cygni had a

PLANETS' BIRTH: CHANCE ENCOUNTER?
The now outmoded "tidal theory" of planet-formation postulated that the gravity of a star passing near the sun would draw out a streamer of the sun's gases *(far left)*. This streamer, it was thought, would separate into globs, and then condense to form planets *(left)*. Scientists today feel the gases would dissipate rather than condense.

planet circling it. Though still unseen, this planet already has a name—61 Cygni C. Since 1942, several other extrasolar objects of the same general type have been discovered, providing a strong hint that planetary systems are quite common.

A still-stronger hint was obtained from a fascinating piece of astronomical detection which might be called the Curious Case of the Missing Angular Momentum. When we look at our solar system we discover that although almost all its mass (99.9 per cent) is in the sun, almost all its spin (98 per cent) is associated with the planets. The incandescent, gaseous cloud that ultimately formed the sun appears to have been robbed of its spin by the creation of the planets. Indeed, if we calculate backwards, we discover that if the sun had been formed without planets, it would be rotating at 50 times its present rate.

Spectroscope magic

Now, thanks to the magic of the spectroscope, it is possible to measure the spin of many stars, even though they are mere points of light in the most powerful telescopes. And a striking fact emerges: young, hot stars have a very rapid rotation—comparable to that of a sun without planets. However, when we arrange stars in their evolutionary sequence, the older, cooler ones show a loss of spin. The conclusion indicates that this spin now resides in planets around the sun. An abrupt slowing-down as one acquires a family is, of course, a phenomenon not confined to suns.

From facts such as these, astronomers have deduced that most stars may have planets of some kind. It does not follow, however, that many of these are habitable. A planet on which life can evolve must be neither too hot nor too cold; it must have a climate that remains reasonably stable for billions of years; and it must have the right chemical composition. There have been many attempts to estimate how likely it is that all these factors will occur, and the answers obtained vary wildly with the optimism of the calculator. Perhaps the best one can say at this stage of our ignorance is that several per cent of all stars—possibly as many as 10 per cent—have planets which are potential homes for life.

This leads us at once into our second great area of ignorance. What guarantee is there that a planet, even if suitable in all respects, will become the abode of life? On this subject there has also been a complete change of opinion during recent years. To the biologists of the 1930s, even the most primitive living creatures appeared so fantastically complicated it seemed inconceivable that life could arise automatically out of nonliving matter in any measurable length of time. One might as well expect the ores in the mine to shape themselves spontaneously into an electronic computer. Even this analogy fails, because the simplest living cell is millions of times more complex than the most elaborate computer

OR ORDERLY DEVELOPMENT?
Another theory holds that planets are formed at the same time stars (such as the sun) come into being. A swirling dust cloud shrinks into a ball with concentric rings *(far left)*.
The rings eventually condense into planets; the central ball becomes an incandescent sun. However, some experts dispute this theory and say the planets begin as globs of dust.

yet built by man. Life, in fact, appears to be a miracle which has no right to exist in a rational world.

And yet life irrefutably does exist on this, the third planet of a quite commonplace star, one of a hundred thousand million stars in our galaxy alone. Moreover, there is growing evidence that at least a form of life also exists on Mars, the world next door. Since a miracle ceases to be one if it happens too often, perhaps the odds against the spontaneous origin of life have been miscalculated.

This appears to be the case. Today, we have very good reasons for thinking that life will rise automatically on any world with a suitable chemistry and climate. To us, in the second half of the 20th Century, life is no longer the mystery it was even a generation ago; after one of the greatest breakthroughs in the whole history of science, the common molecular basis of man and microbe, whale and butterfly, and everything else that moves and grows, has at last been discovered. The biologist now stands where the nuclear physicist stood 30 years ago, peering into Pandora's box at secrets that will shape all the ages to come.

A twisted ladder to the source of life

The chemical basis of all living things is an amazing substance known as DNA (short for *Deoxyribo*N*ucleic Acid*). The DNA molecule occurs in the form of an immensely long double spiral, like a twisted ladder; and the differing rungs of the ladder form a code, as explicit and precise as the dots and dashes of a Morse message. That code contains all the information—the genetic blueprint—describing the creature from whose cells the DNA is taken. One might call DNA a molecular encyclopedia, whose endless reprinting is the passage of the generations.

DNA, despite its enormous complexity, is built up from just five kinds of atoms—carbon, hydrogen, nitrogen, oxygen and phosphorus— and the way in which they are arranged in various, quite simple subgroupings is now understood. These five elements were certainly abundant in the oceans and atmospheres of the primitive, lifeless earth.

In a series of famous experiments commencing in 1952, scientists subjected replicas of earth's primeval atmosphere to artificial lightning discharges, and found that within a week a whole host of complicated organic compounds was produced—including amino acids, the building blocks of life itself. This happened in the laboratory after a week; nature has had billions of years in which to operate.

Although most biologists now believe that carbon-based life of the type that exists on earth must be exceedingly common on planets throughout the universe, this does not mean that a creature resembling man exists on any one of them; the almost infinite variety of living forms in our own world is sufficient proof that nature never repeats itself exactly,

STRANGE LIFE ON DISTANT WORLDS
The prospect of finding life on planets inhospitable to man has started some scientists on fanciful hypothesizing. Starting with conditions thought possible in remote solar systems, they have imagined adaptations life might make, and then have conjured up beings to fit the adaptations. The fishlike being above would live on a water-covered planet.

though it has many favorite basic patterns. There must be thousands of worlds ruled by two-eyed bipeds; but other suns, other atmospheres will produce such endless variations of details that we could never mistake one of these creatures for Homo sapiens—except perhaps on a very dark night.

Though the cosmic possibilities of life-as-we-know-it—that is, life depending upon water—are almost inexhaustible, there may also be whole categories of living creatures based upon quite different reactions. The biochemist Dr. Isaac Asimov has suggested some possibilities. At temperatures hot enough to make iron glow, a fluorine-silicone biology might evolve. At somewhat cooler temperatures (say 300° to 800° Fahrenheit), life might be based on fluorocarbon compounds, with liquid sulphur taking the place of water.

There would also be at least three possible life-chemistries at temperatures far below the average here on earth. In the warmest of these, liquid ammonia would replace water; life-forms in such an environment would flourish at around a hundred below zero. Still farther down the thermometer scale (260 below zero), liquid methane might take over. And finally, at an unimaginable 430 below, liquid hydrogen might act as the solvent in which the multitudinous chemical reactions of life could take place.

Though these are wild speculations, they are not unscientific ones, and we should always consider that life in the universe—perhaps even in our own solar system—may have some fantastic surprises for us. Needless to say, we should find it extremely difficult to study such high- or low-temperature life-forms; not only would the environments of these creatures be instantly fatal to an unprotected human being, but their metabolic rates would be very different from ours. A liquid-hydrogen creature might take hours—or even years—to make a single movement; "exobiologists" (scientists concerned with the evolution of life beyond our planet) studying very-low-temperature worlds would have to be patient men.

From romances to the maser

Until a very few years ago, all such conjectures were slightly disreputable, and scientists left them strictly to the writers of interplanetary romances. This was reasonable enough, because science is concerned with ascertainable facts—and there seemed no way in which we could ever hope to gain knowledge of intelligent life beyond the solar system. The distances involved were so stupendous that both communication and transportation seemed impossible.

Then, in the 1950s the astronomers became aware that the advances in radio technology—particularly the invention of the maser, whereby faint signals can be amplified a hundred times—had given them a tool

TALL BIPED ON A SMALL PLANET
Small planets would possess a light gravity that could not retain much atmosphere. The being on such a planet, according to an artist's conception, might have large nostrils and a huge chest cavity to help him breathe the thin air. The gravity would not inhibit growth or speed, so the being would be tall and would travel in long, easy strides.

LOW LIFE ON A HUGE WORLD
The massive gravity created by a giant planet might produce the imaginary squat creature at right, creeping sluggishly over the eroded landscape. The constant chafing of the corrosive atmosphere would require it to develop a thick skin as protection. Such a being could still be intelligent, however, as shown by its friendly grin.

that could literally reach to the stars. With equipment that either existed or could be readily designed, the communications engineers of the late 1950s could guarantee to receive code (though not speech) messages coming from Alpha Centauri. Today they could do even better; using the bowl of the 1,000-foot-diameter radio telescope at Arecibo, Puerto Rico, we should be able to receive intelligible signals from a range of 100 light-years—that is, over a volume of space containing at least 10,000 stars.

And if this is what human beings can do after little more than half a century of radio development, what might we not expect from races that have possessed electronic techniques for thousands of years? If their psychologies and their scientific interests are even remotely like ours, they would send out signals to advertise their presence, and try to get in touch with their neighbors.

Anybody tapping on the wall?

A great deal of thought has already gone into the problem of establishing communication, over a radio link, with nonhuman but intelligent entities. Analogous situations occur on earth; there is the example of two prisoners in adjoining cells, not speaking the same language but attempting to converse by tapping on the wall. Given sufficient time and patience, there is no limit to the degree of understanding that might eventually be reached.

Research with dolphins—which are thought to have a language of sorts and a high degree of intelligence—may throw light on this question: NASA has awarded contracts to the neurophysiologist Dr. John C. Lilly for his work in this field. Unless we can communicate with the other intelligent creatures on *this* planet, the chances for success elsewhere are obviously dim.

The well-publicized Project Ozma, carried out at the National Radio Astronomy Observatory, Green Bank, West Virginia, for three months in 1960 was the first deliberate attempt to detect artificial signals from deep space. The 85-foot-diameter telescope used was too small to offer much chance of success, and none was achieved. But one day, perhaps, with much larger instruments (possibly the giants that will be erected on the far side of the moon, away from the radio interference of this noisy earth), we shall receive the first faint messages telling us that we are not alone.

There are other methods besides radio whereby advanced civilizations might signal their presence across the interstellar abyss. The intensely brilliant, almost perfectly parallel beams of light produced by the laser could also be used for this purpose. And laser light—unlike radio noise—is something that does not occur in nature; it is light so sharply "tuned" that it would stand out against the background glow of

"Ammonia! Ammonia!"

Drawing by R. Grossman
© 1962 The New Yorker Magazine, Inc

COOL, CLEAR AMMONIA

Somewhere in the universe there may be intelligent creatures convinced that no life could consume the poisonous substance called water, or even live in an atmosphere containing the highly reactive gas, oxygen. A Jupiterlike world, for example, might hold only nitrogen-breathing, ammonia-drinking beings like this poor cartoon castaway.

the universe. Even against the face of the sun, a laser beam would appear a million times more brilliant than the blazing solar background.

It has also been suggested that extremely advanced races might somehow even modulate the light of a whole star so that it winked on and off like a cosmic blinker light. Many stars are variable; but perhaps there are some whose fluctuations are not produced by natural causes. Space may be full of signposts that we have not yet learned to read—because until this decade we never thought to look for them.

Interstellar communication will be a very slow business, as it will always be limited by the velocity of light. A message sent to Alpha Centauri would take four and a quarter years to get there, and no reply could be received on earth for eight and a half. A man who sent a signal to brilliant Capella, 45 light-years away, could not expect an answer in his lifetime. Interstellar communication is, therefore, a project for the ages—not for individual scientists, or for cultures so short-lived that they survive only a few centuries.

Still more ambitious than the dream of talking to the stars is that of traveling to them. Despite the enormous distances involved, this is not particularly difficult—provided only that you are in no hurry. To escape from the earth, a rocket must attain a speed of 25,000 miles an hour; it needs only an extra 11,000 miles an hour in order to escape from the pull of the sun. Anything faster and the traveler is headed for interstellar space. It is a startling thought that the Saturn V rocket could hurl a 10-ton truck to Alpha Centauri; however, it would take a half million years to get there.

To Alpha Centauri in 200,000 years

A fairly modest increase in initial speed would reduce this time considerably; thus a rocket which left earth at 50,000 miles an hour could reach Alpha Centauri in 200,000 years. Very much higher speeds will become possible when we possess efficient methods of converting nuclear energy into thrust. Velocities of at least 10 million miles an hour may be expected in the next century, and this would allow round trips to the nearer stars in journeys lasting about 300 years.

Thus a stable, scientifically oriented society might, as a long-range investment, launch automatic deep-space probes to reconnoiter its stellar neighbors. Needless to say, these robot explorers would have to have a degree of sophistication and reliability that would make our Rangers and other robot prospectors look like products of early-Stone Age craftsmen. Once these space probes had loaded their memory circuits, they would turn homeward with the secrets they had won. Those secrets their builders would never know; they would have been dead for half a millennium before their grand experiment had reached its conclusion.

SIGN LANGUAGE ACROSS SPACE
One of the greatest barriers to communicating with intelligent life on other planets is language. To overcome this barrier, scientists suggest transmitting a series of radio pulses *(blue circles)* at timed intervals. When arranged logically, the series would show a picture like this one, telling a story anyone could understand.

Yet, in this way if in no other, we may ultimately obtain detailed information about the nearer stars; perhaps there are better ways, but at least we know that this may be used.

However, it is not good enough. Unless the psychology of the human race changes out of recognition, men will never be satisfied with exploration by proxy; they will want to go themselves, as soon as it becomes technically possible. The reports of the first successful interstellar probes, or the establishment of a radio link with another culture, will only increase this determination. You may write to a man for years, but you never really know him until you have met face to face. This is also true of contact between civilizations.

A one-way trip in an ark

Manned, interstellar space flight is possible, though only on terms which few of us would care to pay, for it will probably be a one-way journey. Yet it need not be a Spartan journey. At the present rate of progress, we should in a very few centuries be able to build giant, self-sustaining "Space Arks," which would be miniature earths, able to maintain life for an indefinite period. These flying worlds would carry with them all the culture of the parent civilization. And unlike the colonists of the past, the space voyagers would not be cutting all ties with home since they would be in continuous radio contact with earth.

However, such Space Arks may never be built because there are simpler and cheaper—though technically more advanced—solutions to the problem of getting men to the stars. If suspended animation is ever possible, then ageless travelers may pass the centuries in frozen sleep, watched over by robots who will waken them when the long journey nears its end.

Would men volunteer for such missions, knowing that they would never see earth again—that, indeed, some space accident or mechanical failure might slay them in the interstellar night? Judging by past experience of exploration, there is little doubt that they would.

To most of us, such projects will seem repellently inhuman experiments in technical virtuosity; but in other ages, and on other worlds, different views will prevail. Among the millions of civilizations now rising and falling throughout the galaxy, there must be many attempting to colonize the stars. Their motives may be scientific or religious or based on impulses beyond our comprehension—for example, rational beings might find it difficult to understand why we have so patiently stockpiled nuclear weapons equivalent to 10 tons of TNT for each member of our species.

Interstellar travel would obviously become much more attractive if it were possible to reach the stars during the span of a single lifetime. To do this, it would be necessary to attain a speed very near that of light. It is easy to show that no conceivable type of rocket, even if propelled by 100 per cent efficient nuclear engines, could achieve such a performance. But surely the rocket is not the ultimate space vehicle. One of the most common of man's failings is the myopic evaluation of the future in terms of the present. There are no natural laws forbidding us from approaching the velocity of light, and it is safest to assume that we shall do so. At such speeds, the curious effects predicted by Albert Einstein's theory of relativity start to make their appearance. The most famous of these effects is the stretching, or dilation, of time. A traveler in a spaceship moving close to the speed of light would discover, when he returned to his starting point, that he had aged less than those who had stayed at home. At extreme speeds, closely approaching the speed of light, the discrepancy would be very great; spaceship time might record the passage of only months, while years, centuries or millennia would have passed on earth.

This would mean—in theory, at least—that a man could travel to the remotest galaxy and return to earth having, by *his* reckoning, aged only a few days. But the time that elapsed on earth, if indeed earth still existed, would be tens of billions of years.

Though this effect of the compression of time has been the subject of furious controversy in the past, there is now no serious doubt of its reality. It has been demonstrated in laboratory tests of such exquisite sensitivity that they can detect the slowing-down of time on the rim of a phonograph turntable, as compared with the passage of time at its center. (The difference is a few parts in a trillion.)

Callers from out there?

The entire subject of space—from rocket technology to speculation about the stars—leads circuitously but ultimately to one main question: "Where's everybody?" If, during the next few centuries, we hope to go traveling to the stars, why have we not already received visitors from older civilizations?

To this we can give no definite answer, only some plausible guesses. They include these possibilities:

(1) We are the only intelligent creatures in the universe. (An improbable, depressing and downright megalomaniac concept.)

(2) We are so *un*intelligent that no one is interested in visiting us. (Equally depressing, but more probable.)

(3) "They" have tried, or are trying, to communicate with us, but we are simply not getting the message.

(4) "They" are simply watching us, like anthropologists, or perhaps like a medical student peering through a microscope at a bacteriological culture.

FISHING FOR EVIDENCE OF LIFE
After parachuting through the atmosphere of a never-before-visited planet, this capsule casts 50-foot lengths of sticky string onto the ground. Reels draw the lines back inside the capsule. If any living thing—bacteria, moss, lichen—has stuck to the string, instruments record its growth and a radio flashes the word to earth: extraterrestrial life exists. The capsule is named Gulliver, after the adventurer created by Jonathan Swift.

(5) Interstellar travel, for unknown technical reasons, is impossible.

(6) Interstellar travel is possible, but since the number of planets in the universe is comparable to the number of grains of sand on all the shores of earth, we could expect visitors only once in every few million years.

Among these—and other—alternatives the reader must make his own choice. Perhaps earth has had many visitors during the billions of years of its existence, and we may yet find evidence of their coming, preserved in the rocks. One astronomer has suggested that all terrestrial life sprang from the garbage of some careless explorers. This humbling thought is indeed a far cry from the medieval conception of man as the center of the universe.

Some day—perhaps tomorrow, perhaps a thousand years hence—callers will drop in on us from space. And when they arrive, the whole world will know it, beyond all shadow of a doubt.

So now we understand the real meaning of that popular catchphrase, the "Space Race." It did not begin in October 1957, but scores of centuries earlier, with the first watchers of the skies; and when it reaches its climax, the Cold War will be long forgotten.

It is the race to decide whether we reach the stars before the stars reach us.

Rehearsing for the Hazards of Space

From the initial tremendous thrust up from the earth to the shock of re-entering the atmosphere on return, space travel is always dangerous. Not the least of the dangers is space itself. The environment through which astronauts must travel has been described by one scientist as "emptiness permeated by radiations . . . and spiced with meteoritic pepper." An instant's exposure to that lethal emptiness would kill an unprotected man. Even within the protecting capsule there are hazards: weightlessness and immobility, heat, the pitching and tumbling of the spaceship, poisonous fumes accumulating within the cabin, as well as the prolonged isolation a space crew must endure. The total effect of all such stresses will not be known until long flights have been completed. Meanwhile, scientists throughout the U.S., simulating those stresses, are testing volunteers in an attempt to prepare for the perils of a new environment.

PRESSURE AT THE BOILING POINT

Water at body temperature boils out of a beaker held by a space-suited Air Force test subject as pressure in the chamber is suddenly lowered to the equivalent of that at 63,000 feet. In the near-vacuum of space, if a ship were pierced by a meteorite that explosively decompressed the capsule, the blood of an unprotected astronaut would boil like the water in the beaker.

178

Shake and Roll, Rattle and Tilt

Severe physical stresses cannot be avoided during exploratory flights into space and back to earth. Heavy vibrations and the forces of rapid acceleration start the journey off with strains that can cause a man's liver to shift position six inches. A spaceship on re-entry, missing the exactly plotted course, may go into a befuddling roll and tumble.

Earthbound testing of man's tolerance for such punishment is being carried out by machines which tilt, rattle, roll and whirl test subjects in every conceivable way. Three such upsetting research machines, in use at the U.S. Naval School of Aviation Medicine in Pensacola, Florida, are shown here. A giant cocktail shaker (*below*) disorients test subjects; a swivel (*opposite, top*) spins them. A tilt machine (*opposite, bottom*) reveals the subject's visual response to changes in his relation to gravity.

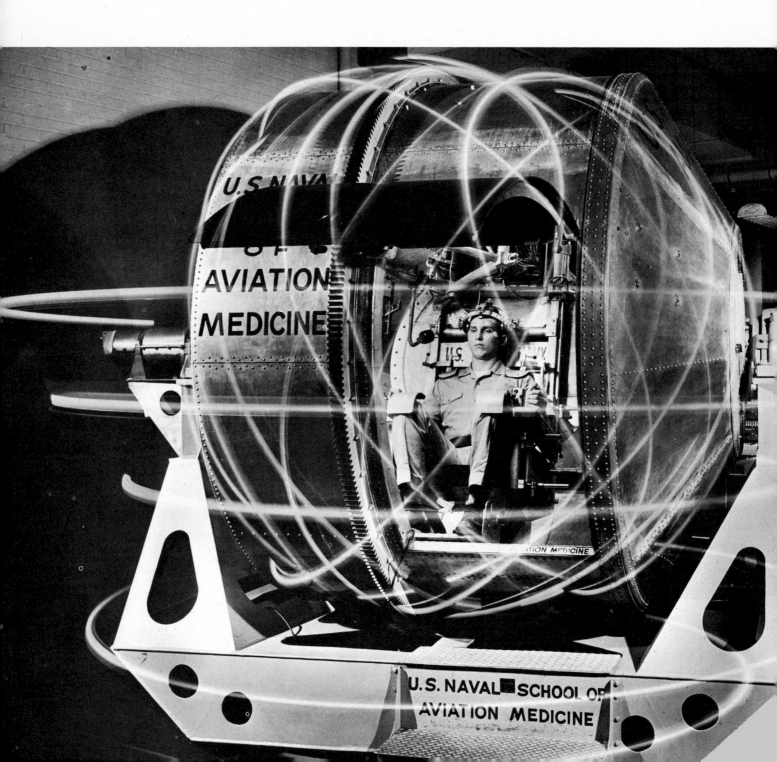

SWIVELING THROUGH SPACE

A rotating chair spins a subject to test the way an astronaut might react if he found himself spinning on re-entry. Electrodes planted near the man's eyes trace the involuntary reaction of the eye to rotation: a slow drifting of the eye backward, then a quick focusing ahead again.

A SPIN IN MANY DIRECTIONS

A volunteer whirls in a dizzying spin in the Human Disorientation Device *(below)* as eye-level television and movie cameras watch his reactions. The device can spin 60 rpm. In this time exposure, varying planes of the spin are traced by lights fixed to the surface of the capsule.

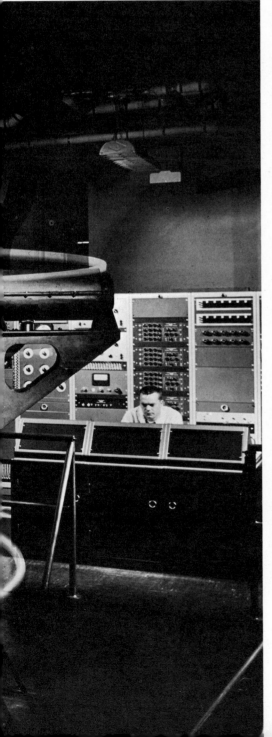

A TILT-EYE VIEW OF GRAVITY

Response to change in gravity is studied by means of a tilt machine *(above)*. The minute parts of the inner ear that detect gravity cannot be directly studied, but their reactions are paralleled by rolling movements of the eye, and these can be measured. A camera trained on the subject's eye records these movements as the eye responds to various degrees of tilt.

MEASURING THE REACH

An arch of yardsticks at Wright-Patterson Air Force Base in Dayton, Ohio, measures how far an astronaut in an inflated spacesuit can comfortably reach. He pushes each stick as far as he can, while a researcher records the distance it moves. Among other things, such tests will help engineers locate suitable positions for the array of instruments in space-capsule cabins.

Equipped for a New Environment

For lunar walks, an astronaut must be protected against heat, radiation and the vacuum of space. He must carry with him a built-in means of communication, a supply of oxygen, water and food, and a way of eliminating body wastes. Yet if he is to walk, adjust instruments *(opposite)* or make a swift escape *(below)*, he must also be light and limber. Special clothing is being tested that incorporates all these qualities. Moreover, for walking inside the capsule at zero g, shoes and floors *(right)* have been made of Velcro, in which one fabric surface catches burrlike into another.

SPACE SHOES THAT STICK FAST
Riding out weightlessness, this man is fixed in position by special fabric soles that grip the surface of the platform. The same material is used commercially as a fastener on clothing.

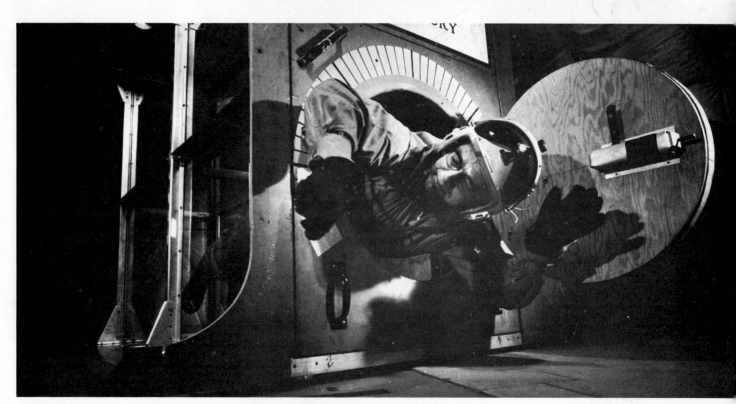

FLEXIBLE SUIT FOR FAST EXITS
Escaping by way of an experimental hatch only 24 inches in diameter, this test subject passes through it in about one second under zero g conditions. For quick action in tight spots, an astronaut's suit must be light, compact and flexible. The six-foot-long escape tube is made of transparent plastic to allow designers to observe the problems involved in weightless exits.

Solving the Problems of Zero G

NECESSARY EXERCISES
Submerged in a pool, a test subject is exercised by pulsating "pressure cuffs." Without exercise, under prolonged zero g, blood would pool in the legs, and veins would soften dangerously.

Astronauts headed for the moon or Mars will experience long periods of weightlessness. Russian and American astronauts have known its effects for relatively brief periods. Thus, until more distant flights are possible, scientists can only guess at the effects of extended exposure to zero g —the gravity-free state in which objects are weightless.

One of the chief dangers that must be avoided is physical deterioration. Even on earth this occurs in anyone kept immobile for long. In space the danger is greatly increased because, since blood will be weightless, the heart will have a much lighter load

to pump. Vein walls will soften. The heart could collapse on return to normal gravity. To keep the circulatory system in trim on long flights, methods have been devised that rhythmically cut off blood flow in the limbs, then release it in a strong surge *(left)*. Scientists studying other problems related to weightlessness utilize moments of zero g that occur in airplanes describing an arcing flight through the air. For the few seconds that the plane is at the top of the arc, anything not tied down will float free *(opposite)*. Then, briefly, the airplane becomes a vital laboratory for dealing with the problems of zero g.

FLYING OFF THE HANDLE
At work in a momentarily weightless plane, one test subject *(foreground)* drills as another cautiously turns a wrench. Ordinary rotating tools send their operators into a spin at zero g. The drill being used above has been especially designed to reduce torque to a minimum. The man with the wrench is finding it difficult to brace himself and work at the same time.

CATCHING A QUICK BITE
As food cubes fly *(opposite)*, a test subject picks his meal out of midair during a zero-g flight. The freeze-dried food pellets in this picture contain a day's rations, ranging from a shrimp cocktail and a salmon salad to creamed peas, beef, a banana pudding and a brownie.

184

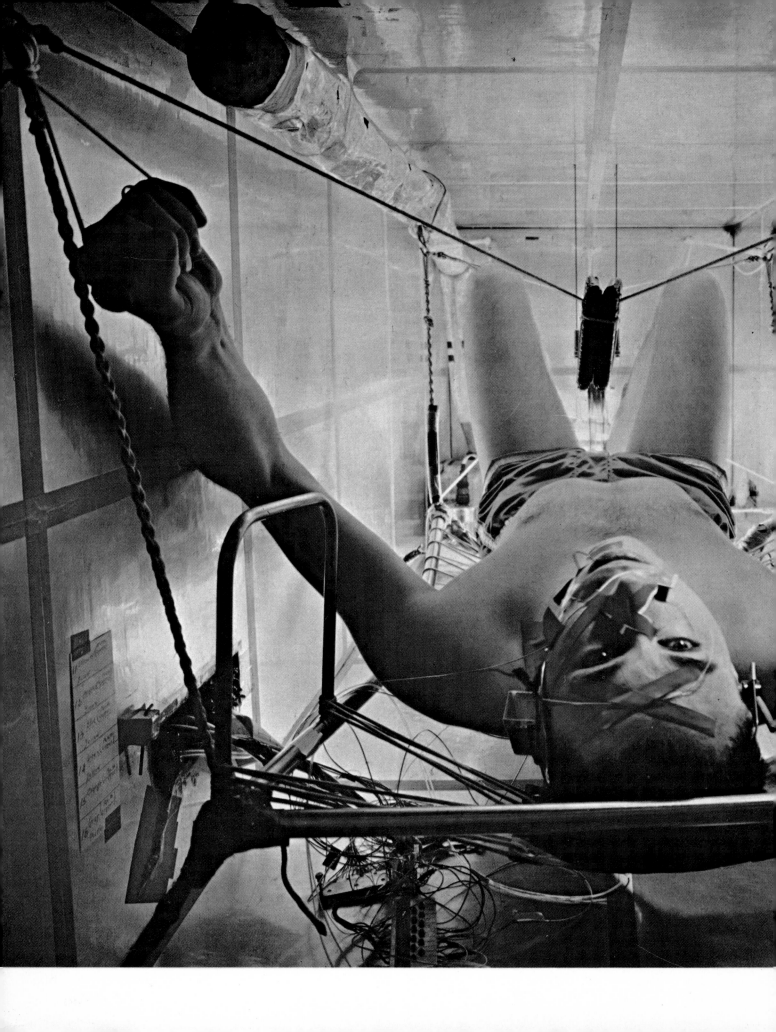

Buoyant Exercise on the Moon

When the first astronaut sets foot on the moon he will have to move carefully. A hop will send him up six times higher than on earth. During such a leap he will be able to perform a backflip with ease. That is because the gravity of the moon is only one sixth as strong as the earth's. A man who weighs 150 pounds on earth will weigh only 25 pounds on the moon; his leaps will be exaggerated, his tumbles surprisingly gentle (a single fingertip will cushion the fall).

To study the problems of moving on the moon, a contraption called a Lunar Walking Simulator has been constructed at NASA's Langley Research Center in Hampton, Virginia. More than 200 men—and a dozen visiting women—have tried out the simulator. The results show that a lunar stroll will be a clumsy process (because of poor traction) but an exhilarating one. The best way to travel may be to bound like a kangaroo. Most offbeat finding: it is easier—on the simulator, at least—to jump up stairs and to go up ladders by hand than it is to go up them normally.

HANDSTAND FOR THE MOON
Suspended from a NASA research device, a man simulates a lunar handstand. Actually, he is almost parallel to the ground and pressing against a low wall *(foreground)*. The effort equals that required to move while subjected to lunar gravity. The camera was pointed straight up.

An astronaut in a Gemini command module normally sees this view of the interior.

Treacherous Tricks Played on the Eye

In venturing out into the distant universe, man encounters new, bewildering threats to his vision—and thus to existence itself. Ironically, some of these threats may come from two sources—oxygen and magnetism—which have been introduced into the spaceship to keep the traveler alive and safe.

The threat of magnetism comes from magnetic fields which may be produced to ward off the sun's radiation during flares or sunspot storms. Magnetism from this equipment may create an effect like that caused by pressing hard on the eyeballs: the field of sight is peppered with glowing streaks or spots (right, bottom).

Oxygen, without which humans cannot live, becomes a perilous poison when it is highly concentrated. A strong dose may cause the phenomenon called tunnel vision (right, center) in which the field of vision shrinks until the victim blacks out entirely. The threat is not merely to vision; life itself is endangered. At seven and a half times the normal atmospheric pressure, pure oxygen can kill a man in less than an hour.

Tunnel vision, pictured here, may be the result of oxygen poisoning or of high g's.

DANGEROUS DISTORTIONS
An astronaut's normal view of his capsule (top) may be distorted by tunnel vision, photographically simulated here (center), or by magnetic spots (bottom). Tunnel vision usually precedes total loss of consciousness. Magnetic disturbances may occur even when the eyes are shut.

Fluctuating high magnetic fields seem to fill the cabin with colorless streaks or spots.

An electrode placed in a man's eye tests the effect on his vision of the various oxygen concentrations an astronaut might breathe.

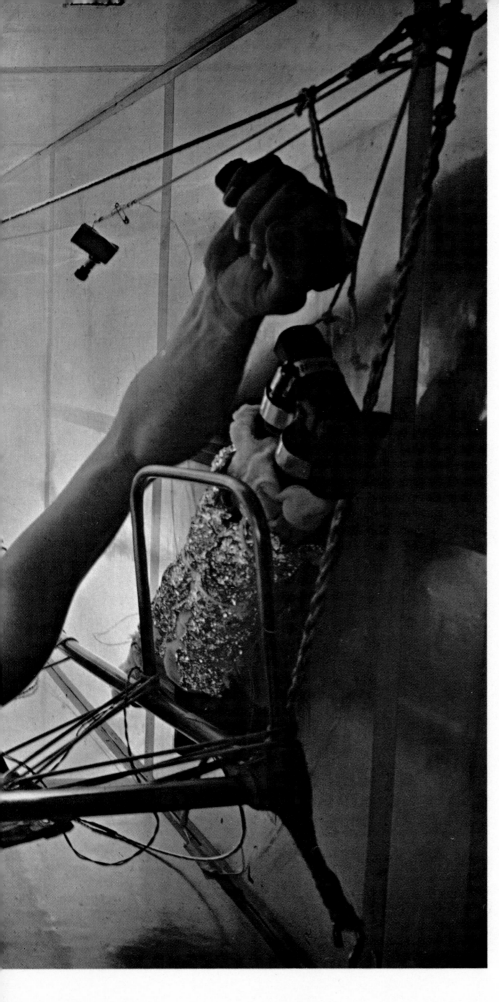

A Narrow Zone of Thermal Efficiency

A spaceship entering the atmosphere at 25,000 miles an hour hurtles within a few moments from a near vacuum, where the temperature of an object may drop to 454° below zero F., into a dense air mass which may subject the ship to a searing temperature of 6,000°. Amid such extremes—particularly of heat—protection of the space crew is an urgent problem.

Researchers have found that a man with no insulation can very briefly endure temperatures of up to 500°. But simple endurance is not enough. Man in space must be able not only to stay alive but to function efficiently. The human guinea pig at left, stretched out in an experimental oven, is providing precise information on how well a man can perform at high temperatures. Such tests have shown that humans can perform tasks efficiently within a spread of only 35°—from about 50° to 85° above zero. Below 50, limbs stiffen; above 85, mental activity becomes sluggish. Thus, although the surface temperature of a capsule may climb to thousands of degrees, its inner atmosphere must be held within a very narrow range.

LABORING IN SCORCHING HEAT
Wired for temperature measurement, a volunteer at the Naval Medical Research Institute works pulleys and pumps pedals with the temperature at 114°. The red tape on his face holds down wiring and temperature-sensing devices attached to his ears, esophagus and brain.

The Vocabulary of Space

ATMOSPHERE: the body of gases surrounding a star, planet or satellite.

ATTITUDE: the position of a rocket, artificial satellite or other object in flight.

COSMIC RAYS: extremely high-energy radiation, originating in the sun and other stars.

COSMOS: the known and theoretical universe, conceived of as an orderly and harmonious system.

EXHAUST VELOCITY: the speed at which the burned gases leave the exhaust nozzle of a rocket.

GALAXY: a group of billions of stars, such as the Milky Way, separated in space from other such groups.

GAMMA RAYS: high-energy radiation of very short wavelengths, produced by nuclear reactions, including those originating in the sun.

GIMBAL: a pivot on which a rocket motor can turn, usually for steering purposes.

INERTIAL GUIDANCE: a self-contained steering system that corrects deviations in a missile's course, speed and range.

IGY: International Geophysical Year (July 1957 to December 1958), a period of international cooperation in many scientific activities, including the launching of satellites.

NASA: National Aeronautics and Space Administration, the U.S. agency conducting America's space program.

ORBIT: the path of one celestial body around another—i.e., of a satellite circling the earth.

OXIDIZER: a substance that reacts with a fuel to make combustion possible; in rockets this substance can be liquid oxygen or some other highly reactive substance.

PLANET: in the solar system, one of the nine major bodies orbiting the sun.

PROPELLANT: in a chemical rocket, the combustible fuel-plus-oxidizer used for power.

RADIATION: the energy emitted from atoms in the form of minute particles or waves.

RADIOTELESCOPE: a powerful, sensitive radio receiver used to study planets, stars and galaxies through their emissions of radio waves, in much the same way that an optical telescope uses light waves.

SATELLITE: a body, natural or artificial, which revolves around a planet.

SOLAR SYSTEM: the sun—plus the asteroids, comets, meteors and planets (and their satellites) which revolve around it.

STAGING: an arrangement of rockets, either one atop another or in clusters; as each stage exhausts its fuel, it is jettisoned.

STAR: a self-luminous gaseous body in space. The sun is a star.

THRUST: the force which propels a rocket.

THE PLANETS: FIGURES AND FACTS

The table below gives vital statistics about our solar system. The first four columns use the earth itself as the unit of measurement against which the diameter, gravity, length of day and length of year of the sun's other planets can be compared. The next column lists the number of known moons orbiting each planet. The sixth column gives the distances of the planets from the sun, not in miles but in a unit which is easier to grasp and may be of more practical importance when it comes to communications. This unit is the time that light—and radio—waves take for the journey, and it can be used to calculate how long might be required to exchange messages between planets. Thus, when earth and Venus are at their closest, radio waves can cross between them in about two minutes (the difference between 8.3 and 6.1), but when they are at their most distant, the trip takes almost a quarter of an hour. The last column gives the same distance in millions of miles.

PLANET	MEAN DIAMETER EARTH = 1	SURFACE GRAVITY EARTH = 1	DAY EARTH = 1	YEAR EARTH = 1	KNOWN MOONS	MEAN LIGHT-TIME FROM SUN HOURS	MINUTES	DISTANCE FROM SUN MILLIONS OF MILES
MERCURY	.38	.4	88	.25	0		3.2	36
VENUS	.97	.9	?	.6	0		6.0	67
EARTH	1.00	1.0	1	1.0	1		8.3	93
MARS	.52	.4	1	1.9	2		12.6	142
JUPITER	10.97	2.6	.4	12	12		43	483
SATURN	9.03	1.2	.4	29	9	1	20	886
URANUS	3.72	1.1	.4	84	5	2	40	1,780
NEPTUNE	3.38	1.4	.7	165	2	4	10	2,790
PLUTO	?	?	6.4	248	0	5	30	3,680

Milestones on
the Road to Space

IT WAS in the late 19th Century that men began to think seriously of sending voyages into the vastness of space propelled by the fiery blast from rocket nozzles. There followed two thirds of a century of theorizing, experimenting and engineering that culminated in late 1957 in the launching of the first artificial satellite. Below are listed some of the milestones that led to the beginning of the space age.

1891—Hermann Ganswindt, in Berlin, draws up the first designs for a spaceship using solid-propelled rockets.

1900—Román Baron von Gostkowski publishes one of the earliest scientific discussions of space travel in the Viennese magazine *Die Zeit*.

1903—The Russian Konstantin Tsiolkovsky publishes his theoretical study of rocket fuels and rocket motor efficiency, and proposes using liquid hydrogen and liquid oxygen as propellants.

1919—In America, Robert Hutchings Goddard publishes a 69-page paper on his research activities, entitled "A Method of Reaching Extreme Altitudes."

1923—Hermann Oberth's book, *The Rocket into Interplanetary Space*, establishes most of the basic theories of space flight.

1925—A detailed thesis, *The Possibility of Reaching Celestial Bodies*, is published by Walter Hohmann of Essen, Germany. It gives detailed calculations for interplanetary orbits.

1926—Goddard launches the world's first successful liquid-propelled rocket in Massachusetts.

1927—The first active astronautical society, the Verein für Raumschiffahrt, is formed in Germany.

1928—In Austria, Baron Guido von Pirquet proposes a system of three space stations orbiting earth, while his countryman Hermann Noordung gives engineering plans for such a station. Meanwhile, another Austrian, Franz A. von Ulinski, publishes an advanced plan for a space vehicle with an electrical propulsion system.

1928—In France, Robert Esnault-Pelterie publishes the book *The Exploration of the Upper Atmosphere with Rockets and the Possibility of Interplanetary Flights*.

1929—Oberth publishes *Roads to Space Travel*, still called "the most important theoretical work on the subject."

1929—In Russia, the Group for Investigation of Reaction Motion is organized.

1930—The American Interplanetary Society (later called the American Rocket Society, and still later the American Institute of Aeronautics and Astronautics) is formed.

1930—Oberth's Kegeldüse, a theoretically ideal rocket combustion chamber, using liquid oxygen and gasoline, is fired on a test stand.

1932—The German Ordnance Corps starts systematic government-sponsored rocket research under Walter Dornberger and Wernher von Braun.

KONSTANTIN TSIOLKOVSKY
Generally recognized as the father of astronautics, this self-educated Russian schoolteacher worked out the theories that showed why rockets would be necessary for space travel. He said that liquid fuels and multiple stages would probably be the most efficient propulsion techniques.

HERMANN OBERTH
Oberth sparked ideas in many space-minded people, amateur and professional, with his 92-page pamphlet, "The Rocket into Interplanetary Space," written in 1923. He later aided in wartime rocket research in Germany, and in 1955 joined the staff of America's Redstone Arsenal.

1933—Eugen Sänger publishes his fundamental investigations into rocket engines in the book *Raketenflugtechnik* (Rocket Flight Engineering) in Munich.

1934—In Germany the Von Braun-Dornberger group fires the first models in a new series of rockets—the Aggregate 2, or A-2, forerunner of the A-4, later called V-2.

1936—The Guggenheim Aeronautical Laboratory of the California Institute of Technology starts investigations of sounding rockets under Theodore von Kármán.

1942—In its first successful flight, a German V-2 rocket sets new records for velocity (Mach 5) and altitude (53 miles).

1944—Caltech gets a go-ahead for high-altitude rocket research and fires its first rocket, Private A, later in the year.

1944—The first German V-2 rockets become operational and are fired against Paris and London.

1945—The first vertical manned rocket flight is conducted in Germany in a Bachem-Natter rocket airplane; in the resulting crash, test pilot Lieutenant Siebert is killed.

1945—The U.S. Secretary of War approves establishment of White Sands Proving Ground.

1945—The Caltech group fires a liquid-propelled WAC Corporal.

1946—The first launch of a captured V-2 for high-altitude research is carried out at White Sands.

1946—The U.S. Air Force Missile Development Center at Holloman Air Force Base begins biological experiments directed toward a man-in-space program, sending up a balloon with fungus spores to expose them to cosmic radiation.

1947—The Bell XS-1 rocket research plane flies faster than the speed of sound.

1948—A nine-pound rhesus monkey named Albert is sent up in a V-2 nose cone at White Sands.

1948—In a year-end report, Secretary of Defense James Forrestal discloses official U.S. space-satellite studies.

1949—A V-2-plus-WAC Corporal combination fired from White Sands reaches outer space—244 miles up.

1949—The first large American rocket, Viking, is launched from White Sands.

1950—The First International Astronautical Congress meets in Paris.

1951—During the Second International Astronautical Congress in London, the International Astronautical Federation (IAF) is formed.

1951—A monkey and 11 mice go safely to 236,000 feet inside a U.S. Aerobee rocket.

1954—The U.S. makes a decision to proceed with Atlas ICBM development.

1955—President Eisenhower initiates the satellite program for the International Geophysical Year.

1956—A U.S. Jupiter C rocket sends a payload to a range of 3,300 miles and an altitude of 680 miles.

1956—The director of Russia's Aero-Medical Research Center reports on experiments sending up dogs in sounding rockets.

1956—The first test shot in the U.S. satellite program, a Viking, is sent up to test telemetry equipment.

1957—In June, the U.S. attempts its first launch of an Atlas ICBM, unsuccessfully.

1957—Soviet Premier Khrushchev announces a successful ICBM flight in August over a range of 3,700 miles.

1957—The Soviet Union launches the first artificial satellite of earth, Sputnik I, on October 4.

THEODORE VON KARMAN
Once called a "genius's genius," this Hungarian aeronautical expert was a great theoretician, practical scientist and industrial organizer. He came to the United States in 1930 and was responsible for many advances in the development of high-speed aircraft and rockets. He died in 1963.

WERNHER VON BRAUN
At the age of 20, Von Braun was hired as the German army's first civilian employee in rocket research and by age 25 was the technical director of all such research in Germany. He presided over the development of the V-2 rocket. When he surrendered in the war he moved to the U.S.

195

BIBLIOGRAPHY

General

Asimov, Isaac, *View from a Height.* Doubleday, 1963.
Clarke, Arthur C., *Voices from the Sky.* Harper & Row, 1965.
The Exploration of Space. Harper & Brothers, 1959.
Ley, Willy, *Rockets, Missiles and Space Travel.* Viking, 1957.
Newell, Homer E., *Express to the Stars.* McGraw-Hill, 1961.

Fiction and Early Flight

De Bergerac, Cyrano, *Voyages to the Moon and the Sun,* trans. by Richard Aldington. The Orion Press, 1962.
†Nicolson, Marjorie Hope, *Voyages to the Moon.* Macmillan, 1960.
Tsiolkovsky, Konstantin, *Beyond the Planet Earth,* trans. by Kenneth Syers. Pergamon, 1960.
*Verne, Jules, *From Earth to the Moon and A trip around It.* J. B. Lippincott.
*Wells, H. G., *The War of the Worlds.* Random House, 1960.

Recent History of Space Flight

Adams, Carsbie, *Space Flight.* McGraw-Hill, 1958.
Alexander, Thomas, *Project Apollo.* Harper & Row, 1964.
Dornberger, Walter, *V-2.* Viking Press, 1954.
Emme, Eugene M., ed., "The History of Rocket Technology," *Technology and Culture* (Fall 1963). Wayne State University Press.

Biography

Lehman, Milton, *This High Man.* Farrar, Straus, 1963.
*Thomas, Shirley, *Men of Space* (6 vols.). Chilton, 1960-1963.

Astronautics

Bergwin, Clyde R., and William T. Coleman, *Animal Astronauts.* Prentice-Hall, 1963.
†Buchheim, Robert W., and RAND Corporation, *New Space Handbook* (rev. ed.). Vintage Books, 1963.
Cameron, A.G.W., *Interstellar Communication.* W. A. Benjamin, 1963.
Clarke, Arthur C., *Interplanetary Flight,* Harper & Brothers, 1960.
Gatland, Kenneth W., *Astronautics in the Sixties.* John Wiley & Sons, 1962.
Krieger, F. J., *Behind the Sputniks.* Public Affairs Press, 1958.
Newell, Homer E., *Sounding Rockets.* McGraw-Hill, 1959.
Ordway, Frederick, James Gardner and Mitchell Sharpe Jr., *Basic Astronautics.* Prentice-Hall, 1962.

Astronomy

†Honegger, Gottfried, and Peter van de Kamp, *Space.* Dell Visual Publication, 1962.
Hoyle, Fred, *Astronomy.* Doubleday, 1962.
Kopal, Zdenek, *The Moon.* Academic Press, 1963.
Ley, Willy, *Watchers of the Skies.* Viking Press, 1963.
*Pickering, James S., *1001 Questions Answered about Astronomy.* Dodd, Mead, 1958.
Rudaux, Lucien, and G. de Vaucouleurs, *Larousse Encyclopedia of Astronomy.* Batchworth Press, Ltd., London, 1959.
Struve, Otto, *Elementary Astronomy.* Oxford University Press, 1959.

*Available also in paperback edition.
†Available only in paperback edition.

ACKNOWLEDGMENTS

The editors of this book are indebted to Dr. Robert Jastrow, Director of the Goddard Institute for Space Studies, National Aeronautics and Space Administration, who served as general consultant on space sciences; to Thomas Turner, Republic Aviation, Washington, D.C.; and to the following persons and institutions: Alfred Alibrando, Public Affairs Adviser, and Louise Dick, Office of Manned Space Flight, NASA, Washington, D.C.; Lewis Allison and his associates, and Ann Bailie, Dr. Paul Lowman, Dr. John O'Keefe, R. Kenneth Squires, Goddard Space Flight Center, Greenbelt, Md.; Richard Bentley, Hughes Aircraft Corporation, Culver City, Calif.; Dr. Franklin Branley, Astronomer, American Museum of Natural History, Hayden Planetarium, New York City; Frank Bristow, Director, Public Relations, and Dr. Eberhardt Rechtin, Deputy Director, Jet Propulsion Laboratory, Pasadena, Calif.; Dr. A.G.W. Cameron, Consultant, Dr. Myron Lecar, Astronomer, Dr. Arthur L. Levine, Executive Officer, and Nicholas Panagakos, Aerospace Science Editor, NASA, Goddard Institute for Space Studies, New York City; James O. Cappellari and R. L. Wagner, Bellcomm Incorporated, Washington, D.C.; Lieutenant Commander Daniel K. Dagle, Department of Defense, Washington, D.C.; Vincent R. Duffy, Public Information Manager, General Dynamics Corporation, New York City; Dr. Eugene M. Emme, NASA Historian, Washington, D.C.; William J. D. Escher, The Marquardt Corporation, Van Nuys, Calif.; Dr. Constantine Generales Jr., Consultant in Space Medicine Affairs, New York City; Mrs. Esther C. Goddard; Mathew Gordon, Communications Satellite Corporation, Washington, D.C.; Dr. Walter Haeussermann, Director, and Hubert E. Kroh, Astrionics Laboratory, Joseph M. Jones, Chief, News Branch, Bart Slattery, Chief, Public Affairs Office, and Herman Thomason, Marshall Space Flight Center, Huntsville, Ala.; Roderick L. Hohl and Donald Raymond, Public Relations, American Institute of Aeronautics and Astronautics, New York City; John P. Keany, Public Relations, NASA, Washington, D.C.; Edward J. Lowe, Public Relations, Sperry Gyroscope Company, Great Neck, N.Y.; Robert E. Mammen, U.S.N. Aerospace Crew Equipment Laboratory, Philadelphia, Pa.; Dr. Edwin M. McMillan, Professor of Physics, University of California; Walter Manning, Patrick Air Force Base, Fla.; Dr. Homer E. Newell, Associate Administrator of Space Sciences and Applications, NASA, Washington, D.C.; John Newland, The Boeing Company, Seattle, Wash.; Dr. G. Edward Pendray, Pendray & Company, Bronxville, N.Y.; Commander Alan B. Shepard, U.S.N., NASA Astronaut, Manned Spacecraft Center, Houston, Tex.; Dr. Kurt R. Stehling, Electro-Optical Systems, Washington, D.C.; Joseph A. Stein, Public Affairs Officer, NASA Division of Advanced Research and Technology, Washington, D.C.; Bruce Strasser, Head, Technical Information Department, Bell Telephone Laboratories; Dr. James A. Van Allen, Chairman, Department of Physics and Astronomy, State University of Iowa; Dr. S. P. Vinegrad, Space Medicine Division, NASA, Washington, D.C.; Pickard Wagner, Public Information Supervisor, A.T.&T.; Dr. Edward C. Welsh, Executive Secretary, National Aeronautics and Space Council, Washington, D.C. The Galileo Galilei translation on page 147 is by Stillman Drake, courtesy University of California Press.

INDEX

Numerals in italics indicate a photograph or painting of the subject mentioned.

198

PICTURE CREDITS

The sources for the illustrations which appear in this book are shown below. Credits for pictures from left to right are separated by commas, from top to bottom by dashes.

Cover—Douglas Aircraft Company

CHAPTER 1: 8—Fritz Goro. 10—Courtesy Simone Gossner. 11—The New York Public Library. 12—Culver Pictures. 13—The Bettmann Archive. 15—Nicholas Fasciano. 17 through 29—Bill Shields.

CHAPTER 2: 30—General Dynamics. 32—Anthony Saris. 33 through 37—Nicholas Fasciano. 39—Lowell Hess. 40 through 47—George V. Kelvin. 48 through 51—Ed Valigursky.

CHAPTER 3: 52—J. R. Eyerman. 56—Barrow from Wide World. 57—Otto van Eersel courtesy The Crowell-Collier Publishing Company. 59—Anthony Saris reprinted courtesy *Popular Science Monthly* © 1954 by Popular Science Publishing Company, Inc. 60—Otto van Eersel. 63—The Smithsonian Institution courtesy Esther C. Goddard. 64 through 67—Courtesy Esther C. Goddard. 68, 69—Courtesy Esther C. Goddard except top right B. Anthony Stewart copyright National Geographic Society courtesy Esther C. Goddard. 70,71—Courtesy Esther C. Goddard. 72,73—B. Anthony Stewart copyright National Geographic Society courtesy Esther C. Goddard.

CHAPTER 4: 74—Ralph Morse, globe courtesy Robert Farquhar. 77—Sovfoto. 79—Nicholas Fasciano. 80—NASA. 81—Michael O'Connell courtesy NASA. 85—Bob Gomel. 86—Sovfoto courtesy Editorial Board for *Sovietski Soyuz*, Sovfoto. 87—Dean Conger for NASA. 88—European Picture Service, Sovfoto. 89—Novosti-Opera Mundi. 90—Ralph Morse for NASA. 91—Dean Conger for NASA—Wide World Photos. 92—Wide World Photos. 93—NASA. 94,95—Walter Schirra and Thomas Stafford for NASA. 96,97—NASA.

CHAPTER 5: 98—General Post Office Engineering Department, Great Britain. 101—Charles Mikolaycak. 103, 104—Michael O'Connell. 105—Charles Mikolaycak. 107—Ralph Crane. 108, 109—Charles Mikolaycak. 110, 111—Anthony Saris, Adolph E. Brotman. 112, 113—Max Gschwind for FORTUNE—Anthony Saris. 114—Anthony Saris—Lewis J. Allison and staff, Goddard Space Flight Center, NASA. 115—NASA. 116,117—Anthony Saris—George V. Kelvin, Jim Mahan. 118,119—Anthony Saris—Dan Bernstein, J. R. Eyerman.

CHAPTER 6: 120—Fritz Goro. 123—Nicholas Fasciano. 124—Culver Pictures. 125,126,127—Nicholas Fasciano. 129—Nicholas Fasciano from paper by Dr. Fritz Zwicky in *Spaceflight*, published by British Interplanetary Society. 131—Robert McCall. 132 through 135—Otto van Eersel. 136,137—Howard Sochurek. 138,139—Ralph Morse for NASA. 140—Ed Valigursky. 141—National Newspaper Syndicate Inc. of America, United Press International—NASA, Fritz Goro. 142 through 145—Ed Valigursky.

CHAPTER 7: 146—Ed Nano for FORTUNE. 148—Charles Mikolaycak. 150—Edwin Taylor. 151, 153—Nicholas Fasciano. 155—Alexander Marshack. 156 through 159—Otto van Eersel. 160—Ed Valigursky. 161—George V. Kelvin. 162 through 165—Otto van Eersel. 166, 167—Geo-Physical Globe by Rand McNally and Co. and Arthur Lidov.

CHAPTER 8: 168—Mount Wilson and Palomar Observatories. 170,171—Nicholas Fasciano. 172,173—Anthony Saris adapted from drawing by Fred Freeman. 175—Dr. A.G.W. Cameron, *Interstellar Communication*, published by W. A. Benjamin, Inc. New York 1963. 177—Charles Mikolaycak. 179—Gordon Tenney. 180,181—left J. Alex Langley for FORTUNE, right Don Uhrbrock. 182—Fritz Goro. 183—Art Shay. 184—Fritz Goro—Gordon Tenney. 185—Gordon Tenney. 186,187—Ralph Morse. 188—Gordon Tenney. 189—Don Uhrbrock. 190,191—Art Rickerby. 194—Sovfoto—Hank Walker. 195—Pierre Boulat—Walter Sanders. Back Cover—Charles Mikolaycak.

A STONEHENGE BOOK

PRODUCTION STAFF FOR TIME INCORPORATED

John L. Hallenbeck (Vice President and Director of Production), Robert E. Foy, Caroline Ferri and Robert E. Fraser
Text photocomposed under the direction of Albert J. Dunn and Arthur J. Dunn

XXX